LOGARITHMS

MODERN MATHEMATICS FOR EVERYMAN

LOGARITHMS

by

K. AUSTWICK

Department of Education

Sheffield University

PERGAMON PRESS

OXFORD · LONDON · NEW YORK · PARIS

1962

PERGAMON PRESS LTD.

Headington Hill Hall, Oxford
4 & 5 Fitzroy Square, London W.I.

PERGAMON PRESS INC.

122 East 55th Street, New York 22, N.Y.

GAUTHIER-VILLARS

55 Quai des Grands-Augustins, Paris 6

PERGAMON PRESS G.m.b.H.

Kaiserstrasse 75, Frankfurt am Main

Library of Congress Card No. 61–18491

Set in Gill Sans 10 on 12 pt by Santype and printed in Great Britain by
COX AND WYMAN LTD., READING

Aims, Scope and Purpose of the Library

The Commonwealth and International Library of Science, Technology and engineering is designed to provide readers, wherever the English language is used or can be used as a medium of instruction, with a series of low-priced, high quality soft-cover textbooks and monographs (each of approximately 128 pages). These will be up to date and written to the highest possible pedagogical and scientific standards, as well as being rapidly and attractively produced and disseminated—with the use of colour printing where appropriate—by employing the most modern printing, binding and mass-distribution techniques.

The books and other teaching aids to be issued by this Library will cover the needs of instructors and pupils in all types of schools and educational establishments (including industry) teaching students on a full and/or part-time basis from the elementary to the most advanced levels.

The books will be published in two styles—a soft-cover edition within the price range of 7s. 6d. to 17s. 6d. ($1.25 to $2.75) and a more expensive edition bound in a hard-cover for library use. The student, the teacher and the instructor will thus be able to acquire, at a moderate price, a personal library in whatever course of study he or she is following.

Books for Industrial Training Schemes to Increase Skills, Productivity and Earnings

To meet the ever-growing and urgent need of manufacturing and business organizations for more skilled workers, technicians, supervisors and managers in the factory, the office and on the land, the Library will publish, with the help of trade associations, industrial training officers and technical colleges, specially commissioned books suitable for the various training schemes organized by or for industry, commerce and government departments. These books will help readers to increase their skill, efficiency, productivity and earnings.

New Concept in Educational Publishing; One Thousand Volumes to be Published by 1967; Speedy Translation and Simultaneous Publication of Suitable Books in Foreign Languages

The Library is a new conception in educational publishing. It will publish original books specially commissioned in a carefully planned series for each subject, giving continuity of study from the introductory stage to the final honours degree standard. Monographs for the post-graduate student and research workers will also be issued, as well as the occasional reprint of an outstanding book, in order to make it available at a low price to the largest possible number of people through our special marketing arrangements.

We shall employ the latest techniques in printing and mass distribution in order to achieve maximum dissemination, sales and income from the books published, including where suitable, their rapid translation and simultaneous publication in French, German, Spanish and Russian through our own or associated publishing houses.

The first 50 volumes of the Library will be issued by the end of 1962; during 1963 a further 150 titles will appear; we expect that by December 1967 a complete Library of over 1000 volumes will have been published. Such a carefully planned, large-scale project in aid of education is unique in the history of the book publishing industry.

New, Modern, Low-priced Textbooks for Students in Great Britain, International Co-operation in Textbook Writing, Publishing and Distribution

In those sciences such as Mathematics, Physics, Chemistry and Biology, which are started at an early age, there will be books suitable for students in Secondary, Grammar and Public Schools in Great Britain covering the work for the new Certificate of Secondary Education and the Ordinary and Advanced Levels of the General Certificate of Education. In all sciences there will be books to meet the examination requirements of the Ordinary National Certificate, Higher National Certificate, City and Guilds and the various other craft and vocational courses, as well as a full range of textbooks required for Diploma and Degree work at Colleges of Technology and Universities.

Similarly books and other teaching aids will also be provided to meet examination requirements in English speaking countries overseas. Wherever appropriate the textbooks written for British students and courses will be made available to English speaking students abroad and in particular in countries in the Commonwealth and in the United States.

The help of competent editorial consultants resident in each country will be available to authors at the earliest stages of the drafting of their books to advise them on how their volumes can be made suitable for students in different countries. If, because of differences in curricula and educational practice, substantial changes are needed to make a British textbook suitable in, for example, Australia, or a textbook written by an Indian or an American author suitable for use in the United Kingdom, then the Press will arrange for authors from both countries to collaborate to achieve this.

National Co-publishers and Printing in Various Countries, to ensure Speedy Production and Distribution at Low Prices

Negotiations are in hand to appoint co-publishers in each of the major Commonwealth countries and in the U.S.A. as well as in Europe, Africa, Asia, Central and South America, to market all books published in the Library exclusively in their country or territory. The co-publishers will assist authors and editors of the Library in the following ways:

(a) By making available to them their editorial contacts, resources and know-how to make the books commissioned for publication in the Library suitable for sale in their country.

(b) By purchasing a substantial quantity of copies of each book for exclusive distribution and sale.

(c) Where useful (in the interest of maximum dissemination), to arrange for or assist with the printing of a special edition, or the entire edition, of a particular textbook.

(d) To use their best endeavours to ensure that the books published in the Library are widely reviewed, publicized, distributed and sold at moderate prices throughout their marketing territory.

International Boards of Eminent Advisory, Consulting and Specialist Editors and Sponsoring Committee of Corporate Members

An Honorary Editorial Advisory Board and a Board of Consulting and Specialist Editors and a Sponsoring Committee under the chairmanship of Sir Robert Robinson, O.M., F.R.S., has been appointed. Some 500 eminent men and women drawn from all walks of life—Universities, Research Institutions, Colleges of Advanced Technology, Industry, Trade associations, Government Departments, Technical Colleges, Public, Grammar and Secondary Schools, Libraries, and Trade Unions and parliamentarians interested in education—not only from this country but also from abroad —are available to advise by correspondence the editors, the authors, the Press and the national co-publishers to help achieve the high aims and purpose of the Library.

The launching of a library of this magnitude is a bold and exciting adventure. It comes at a time when the thirst for education in all parts of the world is greater than ever. Through education man can get an understanding of his environment and problems and a stimulation of interest which can enrich his life. And, too, if he learns how to apply the results of scientific research, material standards of life can be raised, even in a world of rapidly increasing population embroiled in a great arms race. Some of us hope and believe that through education lies the road to lasting world peace and happiness for all nations and communities, regardless of race, colour or ideology. In the history of education examples can be cited of how one or other famous textbook or author profoundly influenced the education of the period. When at some future time the history of education in the second half of the twentieth century is written, it may well be that the Commonwealth and International Library of Science, Technology and Engineering, published by Pergamon Press as a private venture with the co-operation of eminent scientists, educators, industrialists, parliamentarians and others interested in education, will stand out as one of the landmarks.

ROBERT MAXWELL
Publisher at Pergamon Press

Contents

Preface

THIS book on Logarithms is published in the series, "Modern Mathematics for Everyman" as one of a number of books in which selected important topics in Mathematics are developed in considerable detail and illustrated by their applications to practical problems.

The purpose of this book is to provide training in the use of logarithm tables, and in the understanding of the simpler parts of the theory of logarithms. It is appropriate for work up to the Ordinary level of the G.C.E. and National Certificate.

It is intended for the use of:

(1) students in Schools and Colleges,

(2) students attempting to teach themselves, and

(3) perhaps most important, the inexperienced or trainee teachers, and teachers with limited mathematical background who are called upon to teach the subject—many of whom may be unaware of the difficulties which can arise in trying to give children a clear understanding of the topic (hence the detailed treatment).

Thanks are due to the Cambridge University Press for permission to print the tables of logarithms given at the end of this book, to Mr. W. J. Langford for some very useful suggestions, and to my wife for checking answers to the examples.

K. AUSTWICK
Sheffield

Chapter 1

Introduction

LOGARITHMS provide us with a means of simplifying many calculations: by means of them we can replace multiplication and division by addition and subtraction.

In this book, logs are developed by two methods but the text is so arranged that most of it applies simultaneously to both methods. The first method represents the main theme of the book, and the second is merged into it. The first method avoids definitions and theory, and treats logs as an artificial aid to calculation. In fact, this is a parallel to the original development of logs over three hundred years ago by Napier and Briggs. They produced tables of logs as an artificial aid to calculation—especially Trigonometry—without discussing any theoretical basis for them.

Method 2 is more mathematical and requires a knowledge of indices, e.g. the meaning of $r^3 \times r^4$, $r^{1/2}$, r^0, etc. The former method is less satisfactory unless followed up later by a fuller explanation of the meaning of logs, but it may well be adequate for those whose use of logs will be rather limited.

Method 1 may be followed by proceeding through the book omitting Chapter 3, and Sections 4.3 and 5.7 of Chapters 4 and 5 respectively.

Method 2 proceeds as follows:

Chapter 3 followed by Chapter 2, 2.4 to the end,
Chapter 4, 4.3 followed by 4.13 to the end of 4.2,
Chapter 5, 5.7 followed by 5.11 to the end of 5.6,
Chapter 6

i.e. Method 2 is developed in Chapter 3 and the last sections of

Chapters 4 and 5 and then merged with Method 1 in the earlier sections.

The subject is developed in four stages. In Stage 1 (Chapters 2 and 3) logs are introduced by the two methods but all calculations are restricted to numbers between 1 and 10. Stage 2 involves the extension of logs to numbers greater than 10, and Stage 3 to numbers less than 1. Stage 4 concerns the use of logs in calculating powers and roots.

Chapter 2

Stage I: Method I

Multiplication and division involving numbers between I and 10— a simple approach

2.1. Multiplication

We can make use of logarithms as an aid to calculation without understanding all the theory outlined in Method 2 (see Chapter 3).

Let us have a look at the log tables at the end of this book. Notice, first of all, that no decimal points are given: they are omitted to simplify the printing. In fact, there should be decimal points in the first column, between the two figures, and in the rest of the tables, before each four-figure number.

The figures in the first column are ordinary numbers, the four-figure numbers in the other columns are called 'logarithms' (usually abbreviated to 'logs').

Consider the following extract from the tables:

No.	Log
2·0	·3010
3·0	·4771
4·0	·6021
5·0	·6990
6·0	·7782
7·0	·8451
8·0	·9031
9·0	·9542

Certain pairs in the log column, when added together make a third member of the column, thus:

No.	Log
2·0	·3010
4·0	·6021
8·0	·9031

No.	Log
3·0	·4771
3·0	·4771
9·0	·9542

$$·3010 + ·6021 = ·9031 \qquad ·4771 + ·4771 = ·9542$$

These results seem to suggest the following correspondences:

$$\left\{ \begin{array}{l} ·3010 + ·6021 = ·9031 \\ 2·0 \ \times \ 4·0 \ = 8·0 \end{array} \right\}$$
$$\left\{ \begin{array}{l} ·4771 + ·4771 = ·9542 \\ 3·0 \ \times \ 3·0 \ = 9·0 \end{array} \right\}$$

i.e. Multiplication of numbers seems to correspond to the addition of the corresponding logs.

Further cases may be considered,

	No.	Log	
Multiply {	2·0	·3010	} Add ·7924
	3·1	·4914	
	6·2	·7924	

	No.	Log	
Multiply {	3·0	·4771	} Add ·6532
	1·5	·1761	
	4·5	·6532	

2.11. Examples 1

Complete the following and check that the results agree with the rule suggested above.

(1)

No.	Log
2·0	
2·9	
5·8	

(2)

No.	Log
3·0	
1·6	
4·8	

(3)

No.	Log
1·7	
4·0	
6·8	

(4)

No.	Log
1·2	
2·5	
3·0	

Except for slight discrepancies in the fourth decimal place this method will always be found to work. This provides us with a method of replacing multiplication by addition.

2.12. Worked examples

(1) $4·2 \times 1·5$

No.	Log
4·2	·6232
1·5	·1761
	·7993

Looking through the tables we find ·7993 opposite 6·3, ∴ $4·2 \times 1·5 = 6·3$

(2) $3·5 \times 2·2$

No.	Log
3·5	·5441
2·2	·3424
	·8865

and we find ·8865 in the tables, opposite 7·7

$\therefore 3·5 \times 2·2 = 7·7$

(3) $3·0 \times 1·8$

No.	Log
3·0	·4771
1·8	·2553
	·7324

·7324 occurs opposite 5·4

i.e. $3·0 \times 1·8 = 5·4$

2.13. Examples 2

(1) $3 \times 1·5$ (3) $1·2 \times 3$ (5) $1·4 \times 3·5$

(2) $1·5 \times 3·2$ (4) $3 \times 1·8$

2.2. Division

In 2·1 we noted the following correspondence:

$$\text{Nos.}\quad 2·0 \times 4·0 = 8·0$$
$$\text{Logs}\quad ·3010 + ·6021 = ·9031$$

Clearly then, there is a similar result for the division of two numbers, thus:

$$\text{Nos.}\quad 8·0 \div 4·0 = 2·0$$
$$\text{Logs}\quad ·9031 - ·6021 = ·3010$$

Let us check this in one or two more examples.

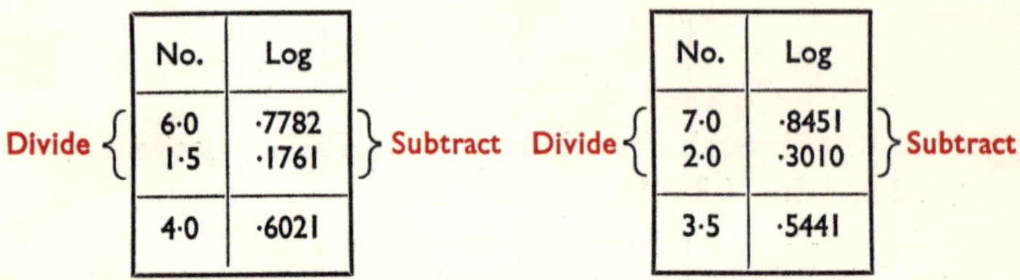

Again, this method will always work—except for occasional discrepancies in the fourth decimal place. Thus we now have a method of replacing multiplication by addition and division by subtraction.

2.21. Worked examples

(1) $6 \cdot 6 \div 2 \cdot 2$

No.	Log
6·6	·8195
2·2	·3424
	·4771

In the tables we find ·4771 opposite 3·0

$\therefore 6 \cdot 6 \div 2 \cdot 2 = 3 \cdot 0$

(2) $8 \cdot 4 \div 1 \cdot 4$

No.	Log
8·4	·9243
1·4	·1461
	·7782

In the tables we find ·7782 opposite 6·0

$\therefore 8 \cdot 4 \div 1 \cdot 4 = 6 \cdot 0$

(3) $7 \cdot 2 \div 2 \cdot 4$

No.	Log
7·2	·8573
2·4	·3802
	·4771

In the tables we find ·4771 opposite 3·0

$\therefore 7 \cdot 2 \div 2 \cdot 4 = 3 \cdot 0$

2.22. Examples 3

(1) $7 \cdot 6 \div 2 \cdot 0$ (3) $5 \cdot 6 \div 1 \cdot 6$ (5) $\dfrac{3 \cdot 2 \times 1 \cdot 5}{2 \cdot 4}$

(2) $5 \cdot 2 \div 1 \cdot 3$ (4) $9 \cdot 5 \div 3 \cdot 8$

2.3. The fourth figure

So far we have multiplied numbers involving two figures only, although the logs have been to four decimal places. We shall now extend the use of tables to three- and four-figure numbers. If a number has five or more figures, we must round it off to four significant figures before using these log tables,

    e.g. (1) 31256 must be rounded off to 31260

        (2) 21·675 must be rounded off to 21·68.

In giving answers from four-figure tables we must not rely too much on the fourth figure.

Thus, from the tables the log of 2   = ·3010

                   log of 3   = ·4771

           Adding these we get   ·7781

whereas in the tables opposite 6 is   ·7782.

In other words the fourth figures do not agree.

Let us consider an example from ordinary addition of numbers.

    3·0244 + 4·5243 = 7·5487

                      = 7·549 to four significant figures.

But, if the original numbers had only been given to four significant figures, we would have had 3·024 + 4·524 = 7·548, i.e. a difference of 1 in the fourth decimal place.

This is the sort of thing which often happens with logs. These logs are correct to four decimal places—they are not exact numbers. Therefore when we add or subtract them it may be that the last figure is not always accurate, and so we must not rely upon it too much. In this book, we shall work with *four-figure* tables and, since the fourth figure of our answers may not be reliable, we shall give our answers to *three* significant figures.

Note. More accurate tables do exist, giving logs to five, seven or even ten or more figures, but these take longer to use and are much more cumbersome.

2.4. Multiplication and division of three- and four-figure numbers

So far we have multiplied together two-figure numbers, e.g. 2·2 × 3·5. To find the logs of these numbers we took the first number opposite 22 and 35 respectively, in the tables. Notice that, at the head of the column containing these logs there is a 0. Thus, opposite 22 we find 3424 and this is in the column marked 0. In other words, ·3424 is really the log of 2·20. If we wanted the log of 2·21 instead, we should take the figure opposite 22 but in column 1 instead of column 0.

This number is ·3444. ∴ the log of 2·21 is ·3444

$$(\text{or } 2 \cdot 21 = 10^{\cdot 3444}\text{—see Method 2})$$

Similarly the log of 2·25 is ·3522, and so on.

For example, find the log of 3·24.

From the tables we find 32 down the left-hand side and read across to column 4 thus:

	0	1	2	3	4	5
32	5051	5065	5079	5092	5105	5119

∴ log 3·24 = ·5105

As there are so many numbers in the tables, it is a good idea to put a ruler along the line which is to be used (opposite 32 in this case).

Now we can multiply or divide three-figure numbers, thus:

METHOD 1

(1) 3·25 × 1·2
  = 3·90

since 5911 in the tables is in column 0 opposite 39, thus:

	0	1
39	5911	5922

No.	Log
3·25	·5119
1·2	·0792
3·90 ←	·5911

(2) $3\cdot25 \times 1\cdot24$
    $= 4\cdot03$

	0	1	2	**3**
40	6021	6031	6042	**6053**

No.	Log
3·25	·5119
1·24	·0934
4·03 ←—	·6053

(3) $1\cdot24 \times 4\cdot25$
    $= 5\cdot27$

	4	5	6	**7**	8
52	7193	7202	7210	**7218**	7226

No.	Log
1·24	·0934
4·25	·6284
5·27 ←—	·7218

(4) $5\cdot72 \div 3\cdot25$
    $= 1\cdot76$

No.	Log
5·72	·7574
3·25	·5119
1·76 ←—	·2455

Notice all the logs have 0 before the decimal and therefore correspond to numbers between 1 and 10. This fixes the position of the decimal point in the answer. A rough check should also be made to ensure that the answer is reasonable,

e.g. $5\cdot72 \div 3\cdot25 \approx 6 \div 3 = 2$.

METHOD 2

(1) $3\cdot25 \times 1\cdot2 = 10^{0\cdot5119} \times 10^{0\cdot0792}$ from tables,
$$= 10^{0\cdot5911}$$
$= 3\cdot90$ since 5911 in the tables is in column 0 opposite 39, thus:

	0	1
39	**5911**	5922

(2) $3.25 \times 1.24 = 10^{0.5119} \times 10^{0.0934}$
$$= 10^{0.6053}$$
$$= 4.03$$

	0	1	2	3
40	6021	6031	6042	6053

(3) $1.24 \times 4.25 = 10^{0.0934} \times 10^{0.6284}$
$$= 10^{0.7218}$$
$$= 5.27$$

	4	5	6	7	8
52	7193	7202	7210	7218	7226

(4) $5.72 \div 3.25 = 10^{0.7574} \div 10^{0.5119}$
$$= 10^{0.2455}$$
$$= 1.76$$

Notice all the logs have 0 before the decimal and therefore correspond to numbers between 1 and 10. This fixes the position of the decimal point in the answer. A rough check should also be made to ensure that the answer is reasonable,

e.g. $5.72 \div 3.25 \approx 6 \div 3 = 2$.

2.41. Examples 4

(1) 1.24×6.5 (3) $8.94 \div 1.5$ (5) $\dfrac{4.55}{3.64}$

(2) 5.24×1.25 (4) $9.6 \div 1.28$

2.42.

Finally, we can extend these calculations to four-figure numbers.

Suppose we want to find the log of 3.684.

We find 36 down the left-hand column, read across to the column under 8 and then use the set of columns called 'differences', reading the number on the same line as before, in the column under 4, thus

	7	8	9	Differences 1	2	3	4	5	6
36	5647	5658	5670	1	2	4	5	6	7

The 5 is added to the 5658, thus

$$\begin{array}{r} 5658 \\ 5 \\ \hline 5663 \end{array}$$

and the log of 3·684 is 0·5663

2.43. Worked examples

(1) To find the log of 7·682

	7	8	9	Differences 1	2	3
75						
76	8848	8854	8859	1	1	2
77						

8854 + 1 = 8855

∴ log 7·682 = 0·8855

(2) To find log 2·747

	3	4	5		Differences 6	7	8	9
26								
27	4362	4378	4393		9	11	13	14
28								

4378 + 11 = 4389

∴ log 2·747 = 0·4389

(3) To find a number whose log is 0·8736:

In the log tables we find 8733 and 8739 adjacent to each other along the line of 74, thus

	7	8	9		3	4	5	6
73								
74	8733	8739	8745		2	2	3	4

Clearly a log equal to 8736 lies between 8733 and 8739, i.e. the number is between 7·47 and 7·48

Using the smaller log, viz. 8733, we have 8736 — 8733 = 3

∴ we look for a 3 under the 'difference' column. It occurs in the column under 5,

∴ 0·8736 = log of 7·475

Note this can be checked by the reverse process, viz. finding the log of 7·475

If the exact value cannot be found we take as near a value as possible, e.g. if a log = 6016 we have to use 6015 or 6017.

2.44. Examples 5a—Method 1

(1) Fill in the blanks:

	No.	Log
a	3·625	
b	4·827	
c	8·660	
d	7·006	
e		0·3824
f		0·7777
g		0·8622
h		0·1120
i		0·0823
j	6·324	

Find x in the following,

(2) $x = \log 4\cdot682$

(3) $\log x = 0\cdot3624$

(4) $x = \log 9\cdot372$

(5) $\log x = 0\cdot0812$

Complete the following examples,

(6) $3\cdot624 \times 1\cdot826$

$=$ (to 3 significant figs)

No.	Log
3·624 1·826	0·5592 0·2615

} Add

(7) $9\cdot612 \times 1\cdot001$

$=$ (to 3 sig. figs)

No.	Log
9·612 1·001	0· 0·

} Add

(8) $2\cdot682 \times 3\cdot18$

$=$ (to 3 sig. figs)

No.	Log

2.45. Examples 5b—Method 2

(1) Fill in the blanks:

	No.	Log
a	3·625	
b	4·827	
c	8·660	
d	7·006	
e		0·3824
f		0·7777
g		0·8622
h		0·1120
i		0·0823
j	6·324	

Find x in the following,

(2) $4·682 = 10^x$

(3) $x = 10^{0·3624}$

(4) $9·372 = 10^x$

(5) $x = 10^{0·0812}$

Complete the following examples,

(6) $3·624 \times 1·826$

$= 10^{0·5592} \times 10^{0·2615} = 10^{----- + -----}$

$= 10^{-----} \quad =$

$= \text{...................}$ Answer (to 3 sig. figs)

(7) $9·612 \times 1·001$

$= 10^{-----} \times 10^{-----} = 10^{----- + -----}$

$= 10^{-----} \quad =$

$= \text{...................}$ Answer (to 3 sig. figs)

(8) $2·682 \times 3·18$

$= \text{...................} \times \text{...................} = \text{...................}$

$= \text{...................} = \text{...................}$ Answer (to 3 sig. figs)

2.5. Antilogarithms

There is another method of changing a logarithm back to an ordinary number. On the page following the logs there is a table called 'antilogarithms' ('antilogs'). We can use these to change logs back to ordinary numbers, reading the tables in the same way as the log tables. Thus, if the log of a number is 0·3249 we find 32 down the left-hand column, read across to the column headed 4, and then to the difference column headed 9, thus

	3	4	5			Differences 7	8	9
0·31								
0·32	2104	2109	2113			3	4	4
0·33								

Thus the antilog of 0·3209 is 2109 + 4 = 2113
But, a log with 0 before the decimal corresponds to a number between 1 and 10,

   ∴ If the log is 0·3209 then the corresponding number (or antilog) is 2·113.

   This may be checked by the previous method and by finding the log of 2·113 from the log tables.

2.51. Worked examples

(1) Find the number whose log = 0·8742.
   In the *antilog* tables

	3	4	5			Differences 1	2	3
87	7464	7482	7499			2	3	5

   ∴ Antilog = 7482 + 3 = 7485
0 before the decimal in a log means that the corresponding number (or antilog) is between 1 and 10, i.e. 1 figure lies before its decimal.

$\therefore$ Antilog of $0.8742 = 7.485$

Again this may be checked by the first method and by finding the log of 7.485.

Thus we can say, log $7.485 \quad = 0.8742$

or antilog $0.8742 = 7.485$

Note that, here again, a discrepancy can occur in the fourth figure

e.g. log $1.993 = 0.2996$ but

antilog $0.2996 = 1.994$

(2) Find the antilog of 0.9542

In the antilog tables

	3	4	5			Differences 1	2	3
95	8974	8995	9016			2	4	6

Antilog of $9542 = 8995 + 4 = 8999$

0 before the decimal in log means *one* figure before decimal in antilog

$\therefore$ Antilog of $0.9542 = 8.999$

2.52. Examples 6

(1) Fill in the table

	Log	Antilog
a	0.8533	
b	0.6211	
c	0.5321	
d	0.1234	
e	0.2829	

(2) If the log of $x = 0.6821$, find x.

(3) If the log of $y = 0.0823$, find y.

(4) Fill in the table.

Check each result by using the reverse process to get back to the figure given in the table. Remember there may be a slight discrepancy in the fourth figure.

	No.	Log
a	3·142	
b	7·80	
c	2·73	
d		0·7821
e		0·4532
f		0·2219

Use log and antilog tables in the following, giving your answers to three significant figures. Do a rough check on your answers.

(5) $3·162 \times 1·195$ (6) $4·283 \div 1·262$ (7) $(2·155)^2$

(8) $8·243 \div 2·1$ (9) $\dfrac{2·33 \times 1·44}{1·89}$ (10) $\dfrac{5·22}{1·2 \times 2·1}$

2.6. Methods of setting out log questions

Method (a) Setting out the logs in a table on the right-hand side of the page.

Example 1.

$3·162 \times 1·95$

$= 6·17$ to 3 sig. figs

	No.	Log	
	3·162	0·5000	} Add
	1·95	0·2900	
	6·166 ←	0·7900	— Find antilog

Example 2.

$$8\cdot26 \div 3\cdot162$$
$$= 2\cdot61$$

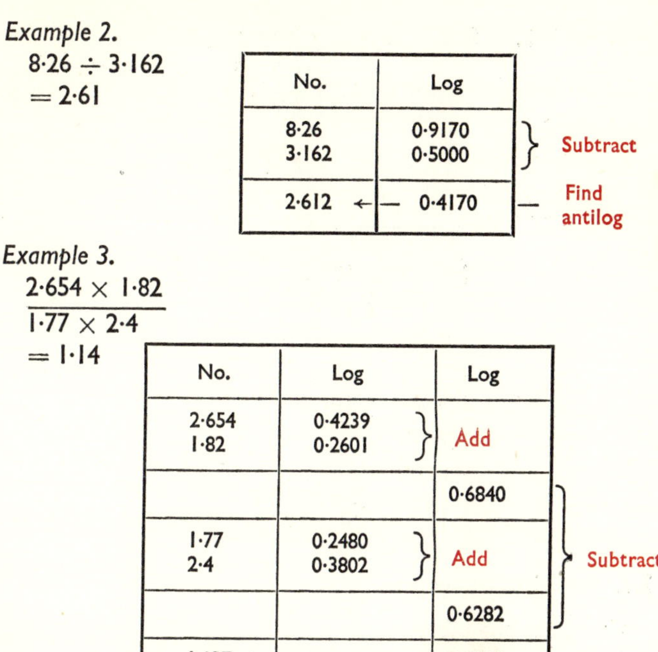

No.	Log
8·26 3·162	0·9170 0·5000
2·612 ←—	0·4170

} Subtract

— Find antilog

Example 3.

$$\frac{2\cdot654 \times 1\cdot82}{1\cdot77 \times 2\cdot4}$$
$$= 1\cdot14$$

No.	Log	Log
2·654 1·82	0·4239 0·2601 } Add	
		0·6840
1·77 2·4	0·2480 0·3802 } Add	
		0·6282
1·137	←————	0·0558

} Subtract

Note. We use the second column of logs in order to make the subtraction part easier to see.

Method (b) Expressing logs as powers of 10—applies to Method 2 only (see Chapter 3)

This method helps to emphasize the nature and meaning of logs, and their use. On the other hand, it can be rather clumsy and uneconomical in more difficult or longer problems.

Example 1. $3\cdot162 \times 1\cdot95 = 10^{0\cdot5000} \times 10^{0\cdot2900}$
$$= 10^{0\cdot7900} \quad \text{(adding the powers)}$$
$$= 6\cdot166 \quad \text{(by finding the antilog of } 0\cdot7900)$$
$$= \mathbf{6\cdot17} \text{ to 3 sig. figs.}$$

c

Example 2. $8 \cdot 26 \div 3 \cdot 162 = 10^{0 \cdot 9170} \div 10^{0 \cdot 5000}$

$$= 10^{0 \cdot 4170} \text{ (subtracting the powers)}$$
$$= 2 \cdot 612 \text{ (by finding the antilog of } 0 \cdot 4170)$$
$$= 2 \cdot 61 \text{ to 3 sig. figs.}$$

Example 3. $\dfrac{2 \cdot 654 \times 1 \cdot 82}{1 \cdot 77 \times 2 \cdot 4}$

$$= \frac{10^{0 \cdot 4239} \times 10^{0 \cdot 2601}}{10^{0 \cdot 2480} \times 10^{0 \cdot 3802}}$$

$$= \frac{10^{0 \cdot 6840}}{10^{0 \cdot 6282}}$$

$$= 10^{0 \cdot 6840} \div 10^{0 \cdot 6282}$$

$$= 10^{0 \cdot 0558}$$

$$= 1 \cdot 137 \text{ (from antilog tables)}$$

$$= 1 \cdot 14 \text{ to 3 sig. figs.}$$

2.7. Revision examples 7

Complete the tables:

(1)

	No.	Log
a	6·42	
b	3·978	
c		0·5582
d		0·3972
e	1·002	
f	2·010	
g		0·2624
h		0·0045

(2)

	Log	Antilog
a	0·3824	
b	0·8295	
c	0·8614	
d	0·0123	
e	0·5821	

(3) $3 \cdot 2 \times 1 \cdot 5$ (4) $1 \cdot 55 \times 2 \cdot 88$

(5) $3 \cdot 162 \times 1 \cdot 954$ (6) $3 \cdot 781 \times 1 \cdot 184$

(7) $8 \cdot 7 \div 2 \cdot 9$ (8) $6 \cdot 82 \div 1 \cdot 37$

(9) $3 \cdot 745 \div 1 \cdot 195$ (10) $9 \cdot 183 \div 8 \cdot 166$

(11) $\dfrac{3 \cdot 2 \times 1 \cdot 5}{2 \cdot 9}$

(12) $\dfrac{4 \cdot 66 \times 1 \cdot 95}{2 \cdot 88}$

(13) $\dfrac{6 \cdot 141 \times 1 \cdot 225}{3 \cdot 168}$

(14) $\dfrac{4 \cdot 294 \times 1 \cdot 777}{2 \cdot 945}$

(15) $\dfrac{8 \cdot 6}{2 \cdot 1 \times 3 \cdot 2}$

(16) $\dfrac{4 \cdot 78}{3 \cdot 91 \times 1 \cdot 18}$

(17) $\dfrac{6 \cdot 774}{2 \cdot 195 \times 1 \cdot 843}$

(18) $\dfrac{1 \cdot 66 \times 5 \cdot 12}{1 \cdot 88 \times 3 \cdot 94}$

(19) $\dfrac{2 \cdot 656 \times 3 \cdot 142}{4 \cdot 18 \times 1 \cdot 36}$

(20) $\dfrac{1 \cdot 422 \times 3 \cdot 162 \times 1 \cdot 99}{1 \cdot 402 \times 3 \cdot 224}$

(21) (a) $3 \cdot 02 \times 3 \cdot 02$ (b) $(2 \cdot 56)^2$

(22) $3 \cdot 24 \times 1 \cdot 95 + 2 \cdot 83 \times 1 \cdot 16$

(23) $\dfrac{3 \cdot 64 + 4 \cdot 8}{1 \cdot 92 \times 2 \cdot 6}$

(24) $\dfrac{6 \cdot 64 + 3 \cdot 19}{6 \cdot 64 - 3 \cdot 19}$

(25) $4 \cdot 1 + 3 \cdot 2 \times 1 \cdot 14$

(26) From your present knowledge of logs, and without using tables, complete the following table.

No.	Log
1.	
2	0·3010
3	0·4771
4	
5	
6	
7	0·8451
8	
9	
10	1·0000

Check your answers in the log tables.

2.8. Practical problems

Worked Example 1

To find the area of a circle of radius 1·2 in.

Area of circle $= \pi r^2$

$\therefore$ Area $\quad = 3\cdot142 \times (1\cdot2)^2$ sq. in.

$\qquad\qquad = 3\cdot142 \times 1\cdot2 \times 1\cdot2$

$\qquad\qquad = \mathbf{4\cdot92}$ **sq. in.**

$\qquad\qquad\qquad$ to 3 sig. figs.

No.	Log
3·142	0·4972
1·2	0·0972
1·2	0·0972
4·916 $\leftarrow$	0·6916

Example 2

Find the area between two concentric circles of radii 2·04 cm and 1·02 cm.

Area of a circle $= \pi r^2$. Concentric circles are circles having the same centre.

Area of larger circle $= \pi(2\cdot04)^2$

Area of smaller circle $= \pi(1\cdot02)^2$

$\therefore$ Area between the two circles $= \pi(2\cdot04)^2 - \pi(1\cdot02)^2$

$\qquad\qquad\qquad\qquad\qquad\qquad = \pi(2\cdot04^2 - 1\cdot02^2)$

But $\quad a^2 - b^2 = (a+b)(a-b)$, from elementary algebra,

$\therefore 2\cdot04^2 - 1\cdot02^2 = (2\cdot04 + 1\cdot02)(2\cdot04 - 1\cdot02)$

$\therefore$ Area between the two circles

$\qquad\quad = \pi(2\cdot04^2 - 1\cdot02^2)$ sq. cm.

$\qquad\quad = \pi(2\cdot04 + 1\cdot02)(2\cdot04 - 1\cdot02)$

$\qquad\quad = 3\cdot142(3\cdot06)(1\cdot02)$

$\qquad\quad = \mathbf{9\cdot81}$ **sq. cm.**

No.	Log
3·142	0·4972
3·06	0·4857
1·02	0·0086
9·806	0·9915

Example 3

If 2·1 g of a substance P combine with 5·1 g of another substance Q, how many grammes of P will combine with 3·4 g of Q?

By the unitary method,

If 5·1 g of Q combines with 2·1 g of P,

then 1·0 g of Q will combine with $\frac{2\cdot 1}{5\cdot 1}$ g of P.

∴ 3·4 g of Q will combine with $\frac{2\cdot 1}{5\cdot 1} \times 3\cdot 4$ g of P.

i.e. **1·4 g**

No.	Log
2·1 3·4	0·3222 0·5315
	0·8537
5·1	0·7076
1·4	0·1461

2.81. Examples 8

(1) Find the circumference of circle of radius 1·32 in.

(2) If the circumference of a circle is 8·24 in., find its diameter and radius.

(3) Find the area between two concentric circles of radii 1·013 in. and 2·031 in. respectively. cf. Worked example 2 above.

(4) If $H = m \times s \times t$, find H when $m = 1\cdot6$, $s = 1\cdot2$, and $t = 4\cdot24$, and find m when $H = 9\cdot91$, $s = 1\cdot2$, and $t = 5\cdot2$.

(5) Density $= \dfrac{\text{Mass}}{\text{Volume}}$

Find the density in g/cm^3 of a substance if 8·5 cm^3 of it weigh 9·5 g.

(6) Find the area of a rectangle 3·12 cm by 2·256 cm. Give your answer to 2 decimal places.

(7) A block of metal is 2·1 cm by 3·1 cm by 1·2 cm, and weighs 9·8 g. Find its volume and density.

(8) A block of metal weights 8·65 g and its density $= 3\cdot8$ g/cm^3. Find its volume.

(9) If 3·6 g of a substance A combine with 4·2 g of another substance B, how many grammes of A will combine with 1·88 g of B? cf. Worked example 3 above.

(10) If 3·23 g of X combine with 6·25 g of Y, how many grammes of X would combine with 2·71 g of Y? cf. Worked example 3 above.

Now turn to Chapter 4, page 39 for Method 1,
page 46 for Method 2.

Chapter 3

Stage I: Method 2

Multiplication and division involving numbers between I and 10— using indices

3.I. Rules for indices

We make use of the following rules for indices.

(a) $r^3 \times r^4 = r.r.r \times r.r.r.r = r^7$ etc.

In general terms this becomes $r^p \times r^q = r^{p+q}$.

i.e. in *multiplying* the two numbers r^p and r^q we *add* the indices p and q, to get r^{p+q}.

(b) $r^5 \div r^2 = \dfrac{r \times r \times r \times r \times r}{r \times r} = r \times r \times r = r^3$

In the general case, then, $r^p \div r^q = r^{p-q}$

i.e. when *dividing* the two numbers r^p and r^q we *subtract* the indices, to get r^{p-q}.

(c) $r^4 \div r^4 = r^0$ by rule in (b).

but $r^4 \div r^4 = \dfrac{r \times r \times r \times r}{r \times r \times r \times r} = 1$. $\therefore r^0 = 1$.

Similarly, we can show that *any* number to the power zero is 1, e.g. $2^0 = 1$, $10^0 = 1$, etc.

We make use of these rules in Stages 1, 2, and 3.

(d) $(r^4)^3 = r^4 \times r^4 \times r^4 = r^{12}$ by the rule in (a).

In general, $(r^p)^q = r^{pq}$

i.e. 'a power to a power' means *multiply* the powers.

(e) $r^{1/2} \times r^{1/2} = r^1$, by the rule in (a), and since $r^1 = r$, $r^{1/2}$ multiplied by itself $= r$. But $\sqrt{r}$ multiplied by itself $= r$. In other words, $r^{1/2}$ is the same as $\sqrt{r}$.

Similarly, $r^{1/3} = \sqrt[3]{r}$, etc.

and $r^{2/3} = r^{1/3+1/3} = r^{1/3} \times r^{1/3}$ by rule (a) reversed,
$$= (r^{1/3})^2 = (\sqrt[3]{r})^2$$

or $r^{2/3} = (r^2)^{1/3}$ by rule (d) reversed,
$$= \sqrt[3]{(r^2)}$$

Thus $r^{1/n} = \sqrt[n]{r}$ and $r^{p/q} = \sqrt[q]{(r^p)}$ or $(\sqrt[q]{r})^p$

We make use of this rule in Stage 4.

3.2. Application of these rules to powers of 2

<table>
<tr><td align="center">Table 1</td><td align="center">Table 2</td></tr>
</table>

Table 1	Table 2
$2 = 2^1$	$3 = 3^1$
$4 = 2^2$	$9 = 3^2$
$8 = 2^3$	$27 = 3^3$
$16 = 2^4$	$81 = 3^4$
$32 = 2^5$	$243 = 3^5$
$64 = 2^6$	$729 = 3^6$
$128 = 2^7$	
$256 = 2^8$	
$512 = 2^9$	

Using the rule in (a) above we can write
$$16 \times 32 = 2^4 \times 2^5 \text{ from Table 1}$$
$$= 2^9 \text{ from rule in (a).}$$
$$= 512 \text{ from Table 1.}$$

again,
$$9 \times 27 = 3^2 \times 3^3 \text{ from Table 2.}$$
$$= 3^5 \text{ from rule in (a).}$$
$$= 243 \text{ from Table 2.}$$

Thus by using Table 1 we have reduced the multiplication of 16×32 to the addition of $4 + 5$,

and by using Table 2 we have reduced the multiplication of 9×27 to the addition of $2 + 3$.

Again making use of the rule in (b),

$$128 \div 8 = 2^7 \div 2^3 \text{ from Table 1.}$$
$$= 2^4 \text{ by the rule in (b),}$$
$$= 16 \text{ from Table 1.}$$
$$\text{and } 243 \div 27 = 3^5 \div 3^3 \text{ from Table 2}$$
$$= 3^2 \text{ by rule in (b).}$$
$$= 9 \text{ from Table 2.}$$

Thus we replace division of numbers by subtraction of powers.

3.21.

So far, this method has worked with special pairs of numbers (those given in Table 1 and in Table 2), which can be expressed as exact powers of the same number, e.g. 64 and 32 can both be expressed as exact powers of 2 and can therefore be multiplied or divided, by this method.

x	0	1	2	3	4	5	6	7
y	1	2	4	8	16	32	64	128

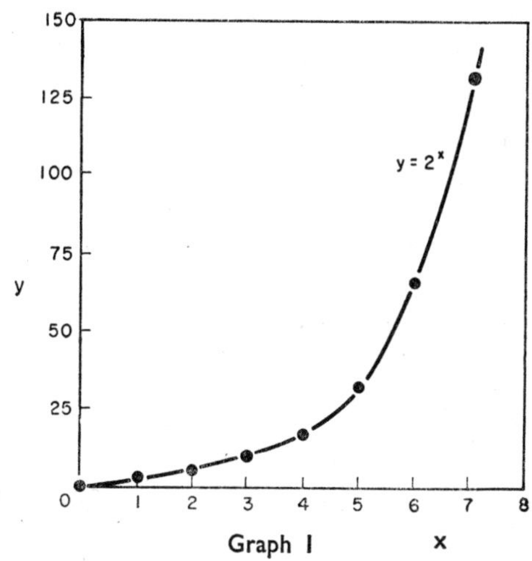

Graph 1

If *all* numbers could be expressed as powers of one particular number, then all multiplication and division could be reduced to addition and subtraction of powers. So far we have a series of numbers which are exact powers of 2, e.g. 16, 32, 64, etc. If we plotted a graph of these we should be able to find powers of two, corresponding to numbers in between them.

Thus, $16 = 2^4$, $32 = 2^5$, etc., from Table 1.

i.e. we plot a graph of $y = 2^x$ (Graph 1, p. 27).

For a more accurate part of the lower end of the graph, intermediate points can be calculated as follows:

If $x = \frac{1}{2}$, then $y = 2^{1/2} = \sqrt{2}$ from rule in (e),
$\qquad\qquad\qquad\quad = 1\cdot414$ (from square root tables or by arithmetical method)

If $x = \frac{3}{2}$, then $y = 2^{3/2} = 2^1 \times 2^{1/2}$ from rule in (a)
$\qquad\qquad\qquad\quad = 2 \times 1\cdot414 = 2\cdot828$
$\qquad\qquad\qquad\quad = 2\cdot83$ to two decimal places

If $x = 2\frac{1}{2}$, then $y = 2^{5/2} = 2^2 \times 2^{1/2} = 4 \times 1\cdot414 = 5\cdot656$
$\qquad\qquad\qquad\qquad\qquad\qquad\quad = 5\cdot66$ to two decimal places.

(Results are given to two decimal places since the third decimal place may be inaccurate—especially after multiplication.)

If $x = \frac{1}{4}$, then $y = 2^{1/4} = \sqrt[4]{2} = \sqrt{1\cdot414} = 1\cdot189 = 1\cdot19$ to 2 decimal places.

If $x = \frac{3}{4}$, then $y = 2^{3/4} = \sqrt[4]{2^3} = \sqrt[4]{8} = \sqrt{2\cdot828} = 1\cdot681 = 1\cdot68$ to 2 decimal places.

If $x = 1\frac{1}{4}$, then $y = 2^{5/4} = 2^1 \times 2^{1/4} = 2 \times 1\cdot189 = 2\cdot378 = 2\cdot38$ to 2 decimal places.

If $x = 1\frac{3}{4}$, then $y = 2^{7/4} = 2^1 \times 2^{3/4} = 2 \times 1\cdot681 = 3\cdot362 = 3\cdot36$ to 2 decimal places.

We will now plot these values on graph 2.

x	0·25	0·5	0·75	1·0	1·25	1·5	1·75	2·0
y	1·19	1·41	1·68	2·0	2·38	2·83	3·36	4·0

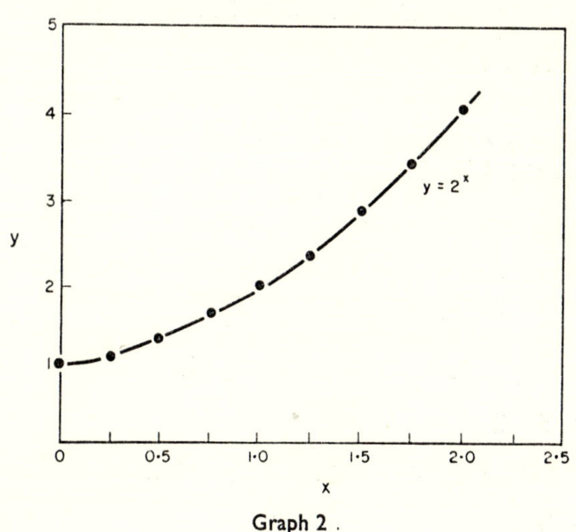

Graph 2 .

3.22.

Notice that if x is between 1 and **2**, the values of y can be calculated from the values of y for x between 0 and 1.

Thus if $x = 1\frac{1}{2}$, $y = 2^{3/2} = 2^1 \times 2^{1/2}$

Similarly for higher values,

e.g. $x = 7\frac{1}{2}$, $y = 2^{15/2} = 2^7 \times 2^{1/2}$

Thus all powers of 2 can be evaluated as decimals if the values of y for x from 0 to 1 are known, the accuracy of the former depending upon the accuracy of the latter.

3.23. Worked examples

(1) If $x = 3.5$, then from graph 1:
$$y = 11.31 \therefore 11.31 = 2^{3.5}$$
again if $x = 0.25$, then from graph 2:
$$y = 1.19 \therefore 1.19 = 2^{0.25}$$

$\therefore$ We could multiply 11·31 by 1·19 as follows:

$$11.31 \times 1.19 = 2^{3.5} \times 2^{0.25} = 2^{3.75}\text{—by rule in (a)}$$
$$= 13.44 \text{ from graph 1.}$$

Similarly, we could divide 11·31 by 1·19 thus:
$$11.31 \div 1.19 = 2^{3.5} \div 2^{0.25} = 2^{3.25}\text{—by rule in (b)}$$
$$= 9.52 \text{ from graph 1.}$$

(2) Thus if we are given two numbers to multiply or divide, we can do this by first changing them into powers of 2.
To take a simple example, 5×4,
when $y = 5$, $x = 2.32$, from graph 1.

$$\therefore 5 = 2^{2.32}$$

and when $y = 4$, $x = 2.0$, from graph 1.

$$\therefore 4 = 2^{2.0}$$

$$\therefore 5 \times 4 = 2^{2.32} \times 2^{2.0} = 2^{4.32} = 20 \text{ from graph 1.}$$

(3) $18.9 \div 4.2$,
If $y = 18.9$, $x = 4.24$, $\therefore 18.9 = 2^{4.24}$
$\quad y = 4.2$, $x = 2.07$, $\therefore 4.2 = 2^{2.07}$

$$\therefore 18.9 \div 4.2 = 2^{4.24} \div 2^{2.07}$$
$$= 2^{2.17}$$
$$= 4.5$$

3.24. Examples 9

Draw your own (enlarged) copies of graphs 1 and 2.

(1) Fill in the following tables from the graph $y = 2^x$

	y	x	Equation
a	3		$\therefore 3 = 2^{--}$
b	4	2	$4 = 2^2$
c	5		
d	8		
e		4	$2^4 =$
f		3·2	$2^{3·2} =$
g		7	$2^7 =$

(2) Complete the following, $3·64 = 2^{---}$

$$2^{1·01} = ----$$

(3) Use the graphs to solve the following:

Multiplication	Division	Mixture of types
(a) $8 \times 0·6$	(d) $128 \div 32$	(g) $13 \times 5·4$
(b) $5 \times 7·2$	(e) $12 \div 6·1$	(h) $102 \div 6·6$
(c) $1·2 \times 3·2$	(f) $100 \div 7$	(i) $62·7 \div 8·56$

Harder problems

(j) $\dfrac{4 \times 16}{8}$
(l) $\dfrac{9·66}{2·1 \times 3·2}$
(m) $\dfrac{4 \times 7·2 + 5^2}{3 \times 8}$

(k) $\dfrac{13·6 \times 4·5}{3·2}$
(n) $\dfrac{5·1^2 + 4·1^2}{3·1^2}$

3.3. Application of the rules to powers of 10

We have shown how to express all numbers as powers of 2—by drawing a graph of $y = 2^x$ and reading off values from it. We can do the same thing using 10 instead of 2. It provides us with a new set of indices to add together. Since our number system is based on 10, it is actually more convenient to work in powers of 10 rather than with powers of 2.

Another name for a power is logarithm. Powers of 10 are often called 'common logarithms'. It was shown above,[1] that if the

[1] See § 3.22

numbers between 1 and 2 could be expressed as powers of 2, then all the others could be calculated from them. In the same way, if the numbers between 1 and 10 can be expressed as powers of 10, then all other numbers can be converted to powers of 10 from them—and much more easily than was the case with 2. We shall return to this in Stage 2; see also 3·31.

Graph of $y = 10^x$ for x from 0 to 1

Values may be determined as follows:

If $x = 0$, $y = 10^0 = 1$.

If $x = 1$, $y = 10^1 = 10$.

If $x = \frac{1}{2}$, $y = 10^{1/2} = \sqrt{10} = 3·162$. (Using square root tables or the 'long' method.)

If $x = \frac{1}{4}$, $y = 10^{1/4} = \sqrt[4]{10} = \sqrt{3·162} = 1·778$.

If $x = \frac{3}{4}$, $y = 10^{3/4} = 10^{1/2} \times 10^{1/4} = 3·162 \times 1·778 = 5·623$.

x	0	0·25	0·5	0·75	1·0
y	1	1·78	3·16	5·62	10·00

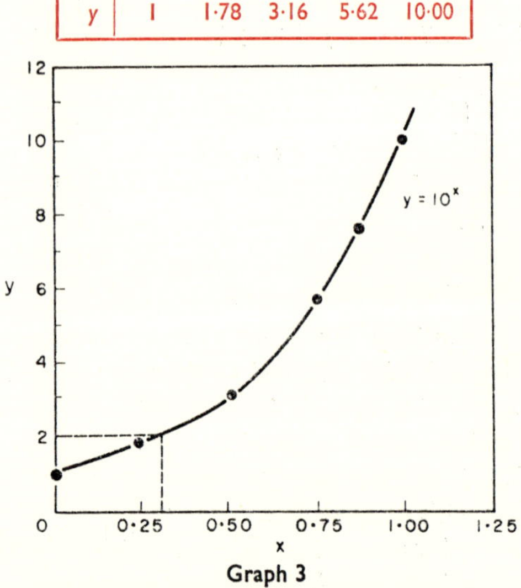

Graph 3

Intermediate points may be calculated if necessary.

3.31.

Notice that this part of the graph is sufficient to enable us to find the logarithm of all numbers,

e.g. suppose we want to find 20 as a power of 10

From the graph, if $y = 2$, $x = 0.30$—see dotted line

$$\therefore 2 = 10^{0.30}$$

But $20 = 10 \times 2, = 10^1 \times 10^{0.30} = 10^{1.30}$

$$\therefore 20 = 10^{1.30}$$

Similarly, $200 = 100 \times 2 = 10^2 \times 10^{0.30} = 10^{2.30}$, etc.

We shall come back to this point in Stage 2, it shows how much more convenient it is to use powers of 10 instead of any other number.

When logarithms are powers of 10, we call 10 the 'base' of the logarithms. Similarly, if they were powers of 2, we should call 2 the 'base' of the logarithms.

3.32. Worked examples

(1) From the last graph, if $y = 2$, $x = 0.30$, i.e. $2 = 10^{0.30}$

$$\text{if } y = 4, x = 0.60, \text{ i.e. } 4 = 10^{0.60}$$

$$\therefore 2 \times 4 = 10^{0.30} \times 10^{0.60} = 10^{0.90} \text{ by rule in (a) of § 3.1}$$

$$= 8 \text{ from graph 3.}$$

(2) If $y = 7.2$, $x = 0.86$, $\therefore 7.2 = 10^{0.86}$

if $y = 2.4$, $x = 0.38$ $\therefore 2.4 = 10^{0.38}$

$$\therefore 7.2 \div 2.4 = 10^{0.86} \div 10^{0.38} \text{ from graph 3.}$$

$$= 10^{0.86 - .038} \text{ by rule in (b) of § 3.1}$$

$$= 10^{0.48}$$

$$= 3.0 \text{ from graph.}$$

(3) If $y = 4.1$, $x = 0.61$, then $4.1 = 10^{0.61}$

if $y = 2.2$, $x = 0.34$, then $2.2 = 10^{0.34}$

$$\therefore 4.1 \times 2.2 = 10^{0.61} \times 10^{0.34}$$

$$= 10^{0.95} \text{ by rule in (a)}$$

$$= 9.0 \text{ by graph 3.}$$

Notice that 4.1×2.2, by ordinary multiplication, $= 9.02$. In other words, the values from the graph do not give the exact answer. This is because the graph itself is not completely accurate.

3.33. Examples 10

(1) Complete the following table from the graph of $y = 10^x$

	y	x	Equation
a	2	0·30	$2 = 10^{0·30}$
b	3·5		$3·5 =$
c	9·2		$9·2 =$
d		0·58	
e		0·62	
f		0·14	
g		0·02	

(2) Complete the following:

    (a) $4·6 = 10^{-----}$

    (b) $10^{0·62} =$

    (c) Common log of $4·2 =$

    (d) $0·56 =$ Common log of $------$

(3) Set out as in § 3.32:

    (a) $2·1 \times 1·5$

    (b) $3·2 \times 1·05$

    (c) $7·65 \times 1·25$

    (d) $9·3 \div 2·1$

    (e) $4·65 \div 3·1$

    (f) $7·35 \div 2·15$

    (g) $1·55 \times 3·25$

    (h) $8·85 \div 2·5$

    (i) $3·75 \div 3·05$

    (j) $\dfrac{4·2 \times 1·3}{2·4}$

    (k) $\dfrac{3·6 \times 1·25}{2·15}$

    (l) $\dfrac{9·45}{2·85 \times 1·65}$

    (m) $\dfrac{2·6 \times 2·9 + 2·2}{1·95}$

    (n) $\dfrac{2·2 \times 2·3 + 2·3 \times 1·9}{6·5}$

3.4. Tables of logarithms

In the above calculations, we have made use of a graph in finding the logs of the numbers which we wanted to multiply or divide. The accuracy of these logs is governed by the accuracy of the graph drawn, and does not extend to many decimal places. In order to save time in finding logs and to obtain more accurate values, the logs of numbers from 1 to 10 have been calculated and tabulated.

The most popular tables of logs are calculated to four decimal places for four-figure numbers. Since the logs of numbers between 1 and 10 are themselves *all* decimals between 0 and 1 the decimal points are often omitted in tables—for convenience in printing. Again, as mentioned above, the logs of all numbers can be determined from those of numbers between 1 and 10. Decimals are therefore omitted in the numbers as well as the logs. Thus 2·0 and 20 are not distinguished in the tables. We shall return to this fact again in the next Stage.

It is useful to compare a few values from the tables with those from graph 3, before going on to use the tables:

From the graph, when $y = 2$, $x = 0.30$

    i.e. $2 = 10^{0.30}$ or log $2 = 0.30$

From the tables, opposite 20 we find 3010

    i.e. log $2.0 = 0.3010$

i.e. if the graph had been larger, thus giving greater accuracy, we should have found $x = 0.3010$ when $y = 2$

Again from the graph, when $y = 0.60$

    i.e. $4 = 10^{0.60}$ or log $4 = 0.60$;

from the tables, opposite 40 we find 6021, i.e. log $4.0 = 0.6021$. Here again 0·6021 is a more accurate value of log 4 than the 0·60 from the graph.

Notice that we say 0·6021 is *more* accurate, it is still not *exact*. The table gives a value correct to 4 decimal places, not an exact value. In fact, powers rarely work out to be exact decimals.

Thus we may now write:

$2.0 \times 4.0 = 10^{0.3010} \times 10^{0.6021} = 10^{0.9031} = 8.0$, since 0·9031 occurs opposite 8·0 (using the tables in reverse this time).

Numbers between 1 and 10 have logs between 0 and 1, and vice-versa. It should be noted that this very simple problem is merely used as an illustration of how to use the tables. Tables are designed to make calculations easier not harder, and should only be so used once the techniques have been mastered.

D

3.41. Further worked examples

$2 \cdot 0 \times 3 \cdot 5 = 10^{0 \cdot 3010} \times 10^{0 \cdot 5441}$ (2 and 20, and 3·5 and 35, are the same in the tables)

$$= 10^{0 \cdot 8451}$$

$$= 7 \cdot 0 \text{ using the tables in reverse}$$

$2 \cdot 2 \times 3 \cdot 5 = 10^{0 \cdot 3424} \times 10^{0 \cdot 5441}$

$$= 10^{0 \cdot 8865}$$

$$= 7 \cdot 7$$

$6 \cdot 0 \div 1 \cdot 5 = 10^{0 \cdot 7782} \div 10^{0 \cdot 1761} = 10^{0 \cdot 7782 - 0 \cdot 1761} = 10^{0 \cdot 6021} = 4 \cdot 0$

3.42. Examples II

Using tables.

(1) $3 \times 1 \cdot 5$	(4) $3 \times 1 \cdot 8$	(7) $5 \cdot 2 \div 1 \cdot 3$
(2) $1 \cdot 5 \times 3 \cdot 2$	(5) $1 \cdot 4 \times 3 \cdot 5$	(8) $5 \cdot 6 \div 1 \cdot 6$
(3) $1 \cdot 2 \times 3$	(6) $7 \cdot 6 \div 2 \cdot 0$	(9) $9 \cdot 5 \div 3 \cdot 8$
		(10) $\dfrac{3 \cdot 2 \times 1 \cdot 5}{2 \cdot 4}$

3.5. The fourth figure

So far we have multiplied numbers involving two figures only, although the logs have been to four decimal places. We shall now extend the use of tables to three- and four-figure numbers. If a number has five or more figures, we must round it off to four significant figures before using these log tables,

    e.g. (1) 31256 must be rounded off to 31260

        (2) 21·675 must be rounded off to 21·68

In giving answers from four-figure tables we must not rely too much on the fourth figure.

Thus, from the tables the log of $2 = 0 \cdot 3010$

                                log of $3 = 0 \cdot 4771$

$\therefore 2 = 10^{0 \cdot 3010} \qquad 3 = 10^{0 \cdot 4771}$

$\therefore 2 \times 3 = 10^{0 \cdot 3010} \times 10^{0 \cdot 4771} = 10^{0 \cdot 7781}$

But from the tables, the log of $6 = 0 \cdot 7782$

    i.e. $6 = 10^{0 \cdot 7782}$

In other words the fourth figures do not agree.

Let us consider an example from ordinary addition of numbers.

$$3 \cdot 0244 + 4 \cdot 5243 = 7 \cdot 5487$$

$$= 7 \cdot 549 \text{ to four significant figures.}$$

But if the original numbers had only been given to four significant figures, we would have had $3 \cdot 024 + 4 \cdot 524 = 7 \cdot 548$

i.e. a difference of 1 in the fourth decimal place.

This is the sort of thing which often happens with logs. These logs are correct to four decimal places—they are not exact numbers. Therefore when we add or subtract them it may be that the last figure is not always accurate, and so we must not rely upon it too much. In this book, we shall work with *four*-figure tables and since the fourth figure of our answers may not be reliable, we shall give our answers to *three* significant figures.

Note. More accurate tables do exist, giving logs to five, seven or even ten or more figures, but these take longer to use and are much more cumbersome.

3.6. Now turn to 2.4, page 8, and continue to the end of Chapter 2

Chapter 4

Stage 2

Multiplication and division involving numbers greater than 10

So far all our calculations have been restricted to numbers between 1 and 10. Let us now extend our use of logs to numbers greater than 10.

4.1. Method 1 *(for Method 2 see 4.3, page 46)*

Numbers between 1 and 10 have been used so far and their logs have been of the form zero followed by a four-figure decimal.

4.11.

Two special cases are worth considering before we proceed to numbers greater than 10.

Log 1

Any positive number divided by itself equals 1, e.g. $4 \div 4 = 1$. ∴ if we subtract log 4 from log 4 we shall get log 1. But log 4 — log 4 obviously equals zero.

∴ log 1 = 0.

Log 10

Since $2 \times 5 = 10$,

log $(2 \times 5) = $ log 10

∴ log 2 + log 5 = log 10

∴ log 10 = 1

No.	Log
2·0	0·3010
5·0	0·6990
	1·0000

As numbers increase from 1 to 10, their logs increase from 0 to 1.

4.12.

Logs of numbers greater than 10.
$4 \times 10 = 40,$
$\therefore \log (4 \times 10) = \log 40$

$\therefore \log 40 = 1{\cdot}6021$

No.	Log
4·0	0·6021
10·0	1·0000
	1·6021

$40 \times 10 = 400$
$\therefore \log (40 \times 10) = \log 400$

$\therefore \log 400 = 2{\cdot}6021$

No.	Log
40·0	1·6021
10·0	1·0000
	2·6021

Similarly, we can show that log 4000 = 3·6021, log 40000 = 4·6021, etc.

These results can be summarized as follows:

In the same way we could get:

	No.	Log
a	4·000	0·6021
b	40·00	1·6021
c	400·0	2·6021
d	4000·	3·6021
e	40000·	4·6021

	No.	Log
a	1·200	0·0792
b	12·00	1·0792
c	120·0	2·0792
d	1200·	3·0792
e	12000·	4·0792

In each of these tables, on line (a) the number and log are like the ones we have used already in Chapter 2, i.e. the number is between 1 and 10.

On line (b), the log is the same as on line (a) except for a 1 in front of the decimal. The number comes from the one on line (a) by moving the decimal *one* place to the right.

On line (c), the log is the same as line (a) except for a **2** in front of the decimal. The number comes from the one on line (a) by moving the decimal *two* places to the right.

e.g. 4·000 ⟶ 400·0

1·200 ⟶ 120·0

On line (d), the log is the same as on line (a) except for a **3** in front of the decimal. The number comes from the one on line (a) by moving the decimal *three* places to the right.

e.g. 4·000 ⟶ 4000·

1·200 ⟶ 1200·

. . . . and so on

Thus, to find the log of a number greater than 10, e.g. 526·3, first write it as a number between 1 and 10, i.e. put the decimal after the first figure, thus 5·263 (this is called putting a number in *Standard Form*). Find the log of this number, log 5·263 = 0·7212. Then count up the number of places the decimal point must move to get back to its original position—from 5·263 to 526·3, i.e. *two* places, ∴ put **2** in front of the log.

Thus, log 526·3 = 2·7212.

Example 1. To find log 482·7

In standard form the number is 4·827

log 4·827 = 0·6836

4·827 ⟶ 482·7 means move the decimal *two* places to the right, ∴ put **2** in front of the log.

thus, log 482·7 = 2·6836.

Example 2. To find log 26·38

In standard form the number is 2·638

log 2·638 = 0·4213

2·638 ⟶ 26·38 means move the decimal *one* place to the right, ∴ put **1** in front of the log.

thus, log 26·38 = 1·4213.

Example 3. To find log 468200

In standard form the number is 4·682

log 4·682 = 0·6704

4·682 ⟶ 468200 means move the decimal *five* places to the right,

∴ put **5** in front of the log.
thus, log 468200 = 5·6704

4.13. Antilogs for numbers greater than 10

To find the antilog we simply reverse the above argument, e.g. taking the result of Example 2 above, let us find the antilog of 1·4213:

> antilog of 0·4213 = 2·638 which is in Standard form; then the **1** in front of the 0·4213 means move the decimal in 2·638 *one* place to the right ∴ antilog of 1·4213 = 26·38
>
> *Example*: To find the antilog of 3·1628
> Antilog of 0·1628 = 1·455 which is in standard form. The **3** in front of the 0·1628 means move the decimal point in 1·455 *three* places to the right,
> ∴ antilog of 3·1628 = 1455.

4.14.

The decimal part of a log is called the *mantissa*, and the figure in front of the decimal is called the *characteristic*.

4.15. Further worked examples

(1) To find the log of 286·3
> In standard form the number is 2·863
> log 2·863 = 0·4569
> 2·863 ⟶ 286·3 means move the decimal *two* places to the right, ∴ put **2** in front of the decimal in the log.
> thus, log 286·3 = 2·4569.

(2) To find *x* given that log *x* = 3·2845
> Antilog of 0·2845 = 1·925 which is in standard form. The **3** in front of the decimal in the log means move the decimal point in 1·925 three places to the right,
> ∴ antilog 3·2845 = 1925.
> i.e. *x* = 1925.

(3) To find *x* if log *x* = 5·2845
> As in example (2), antilog 0·2845 = 1·925.
> The **5** in front of the decimal in the log means move the

decimal point in 1·925 *five* places to the right,

∴ antilog 5·2845 = 192500, i.e. add on zeros until the decimal has moved the required number of places.

∴ x = 192500.

4.16. Examples 12

(1) Complete the table:

	No.	Log
a	3·162	
b	14·95	
c	3872·	
d	149·7	
e	52800·	
f		3·1684
g		0·1952
h		7·3224
i		1·7845

(2) log x = 4·5642. Find x

(3) Find log 367·2

(4) Find log 82543 as accurately as tables permit

(5) log x = 3·0100. Find x

4.17. Worked examples

(1) 38·25 × 124·6

= 4770 (to 3 sig. figs)

No.	Log	
38·25	1·5827	} Add
124·6	2·0955	
4766· ←	3·6782	First find antilog of 0·6782

(2) 563·2 ÷ 12·67

= 44·5

No.	Log	
563·2	2·7507	} Subtract
12·67	1·1028	
44·45 ←	1·6479	First find antilog of 0·6479

4.18. Examples 13 (give your answers to 3 sig. figs.)

(1) $68\cdot24 \times 2\cdot952$

(2) $372\cdot5 \times 19\cdot64$

(3) $8284 \times 19\cdot28$

(4) $59\cdot72 \times 188\cdot5$

(5) $37824 \times 1\cdot928$

(6) $\dfrac{57\cdot6}{37\cdot2}$

(7) $\dfrac{882\cdot6}{33\cdot24}$

(8) $\dfrac{98210}{453\cdot7}$

(9) $\dfrac{88\cdot66 \times 1\cdot923}{47\cdot66}$

(10) $\dfrac{1283 \times 19\cdot6 \times 37}{28\cdot6}$

(11) $\dfrac{3824 \times 79\cdot2}{37\cdot6 \times 148\cdot2}$

(12) $\dfrac{88\cdot24 \times 37\cdot6 \times 19\cdot2}{187\cdot3 \times 52\cdot9}$

4.2. Practical applications

Example 1

Find the volume of a cylinder of height $119\cdot1$ cm and radius $33\cdot6$ cm

$$V = \pi r^2 h$$
$$= 3\cdot142 \times 33\cdot6^2 \times 119\cdot1$$
$$= 3\cdot142 \times 33\cdot6 \times 33\cdot6$$
$$\times 119\cdot1$$
$$= 422000 \text{ cm}^3$$

No.	Log	
3·142	0·4972	
33·6	1·5263	Add
33·6	1·5263	
119·1	2·0759	
422400	5·6257	

Example 2

Find the density of a block $36\cdot2$ cm by $19\cdot6$ cm by $1\cdot48$ cm and weighing 1927 g.

Density = Mass/Volume

Volume = $36\cdot2 \times 19\cdot6 \times 1\cdot48$ cm^3

$$\therefore \text{Density} = \frac{1927}{36 \cdot 2 \times 19 \cdot 6 \times 1 \cdot 48} \quad \text{g/cm}^3$$

$$= 1 \cdot 84 \text{ g/cm}^3$$

No.	Log	Log	
1927		3·2849	
36·2 19·6 1·48	1·5587 1·2923 0·1703	Add	Sub- tract
		3·0213	
1·835		0·2636	

4.21. Examples 14

(1) Find the area of curved surface of a cylinder of radius 2·3 in. and height 19·4 in. (Area $= 2\pi rh$).

(2) Find the volume and density of a cylinder of height 9·2 cm and radius 2·8 cm if it weighs 648·3 g.

(3) Find the simple interest on £982 for 6·5 yrs at 2·75%.

(4) Find the radius of a circular running track of 880 yds circumference

(5) Find the number of revolutions per mile of a bicycle wheel of diameter 26 in.

(6) If $H = mst$, find H when $m = 28 \cdot 6$, $s = 1 \cdot 95$, and $t = 37 \cdot 2$.

(7) If $H = mst$, find s if $H = 5684$, $m = 38 \cdot 7$, and $t = 52 \cdot 1$.

(8) Express 62·85 : 19·41 in the form n : 1.

(9) Find the area of this right-angled triangle.

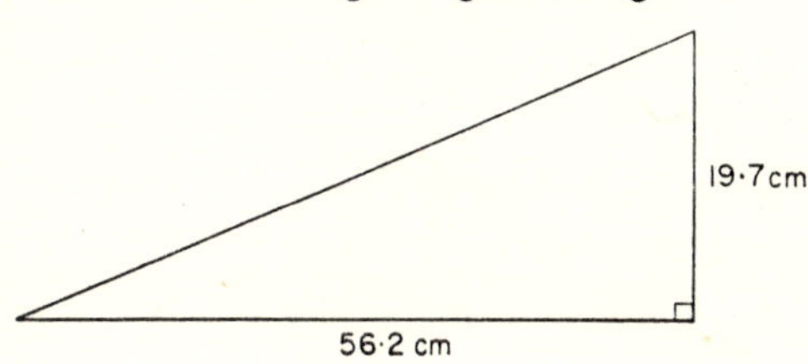

(10) Find the distance travelled in 37 min by the tip of a 6 in. minute hand of a clock.

Now turn to Chapter 5, page 49 for Method 1
page 67 for Method 2

4.3. Method 2 (*for numbers greater than* 10)

From tables we get $\log 4 = 0.6021$, which means that $4 = 10^{0.6021}$
But $40 = 10 \times 4 = 10^1 \times 10^{0.6021}$
$\qquad\qquad = 10^{1.6021}$ by the rules for indices.
But, if $40 = 10^{1.6021}$, then $\log 40 = 1.6021$
Similarly $400 = 100 \times 4 = 10^2 \times 10^{0.6021}$
$\qquad\qquad\qquad = 10^{2.6021}$

$\therefore \log 400 = 2.6021$
Similarly, $\log 4000 = 3.6021$
and $\log 40000 = 4.6021$
These results may be tabulated as follows:

	No.		Log
a	4	4	0·6021
b	40	4×10^1	1·6021
c	400	4×10^2	2·6021
d	4000	4×10^3	3·6021
e	40000	4×10^4	4·6021

Thus in each case the decimal part of the log is the same, only the number in front of it changes.
In the same way, since $\log 1.2 = 0.0792$, we should get:

	No.		Log
a	1·2	1·2	0·0792
b	12	$1·2 \times 10^1$	1·0792
c	120	$1·2 \times 10^2$	2·0792
d	1200	$1·2 \times 10^3$	3·0792
e	12000	$1·2 \times 10^4$	4·0792

In each of these tables, on line (a) the number and the log are like the ones we have used already in Chapter 2, i.e. the number is between 1 and 10.

On the line (b), the log is the same as on line (a) except for a **1** in front of the decimal. The number comes from the one on line (a) by moving the decimal *one* place to the right. On line (c), the log is the same as line (a) except for a **2** in front of the decimal. The number comes from the one on line (a) by moving the decimal *two* places to the right.

e.g. 4·000 ⟶ 400·0

1·200 ⟶ 120·0

On line (d) the log is the same as on line (a) except for a **3** in front of the decimal. The number comes from the one on line (a) by moving the decimal *three* places to the right.

e.g. 4·000 ⟶ 4000

1·200 ⟶ 1200

Thus, to find the log of a number greater than 10, e.g. 526·3, first write it as a number between 1 and 10, i.e. put the decimal after the first figure, thus 5·263 (this is called putting a number in *Standard Form*). Find the log of this number, log 5·263 = 0·7212. Then count up the number of places the decimal point must move to get back to its original position—from 5·263 to 526·3, i.e. *two* places, ∴ put **2** in front of the log. Thus, log 526·3 = 2·7212.

Note: The middle column of the above tables shows how standard form is obtained.

Example 1. To find log 482·7

In standard form the number is 4·827

log 4·827 = 0·6836

4·827 ⟶ 482·7 means moving the decimal *two* places to the right, ∴ put **2** in front of the log.

thus, log 482·7 = 2·6836.

Example 2. To find log 26·38

In standard form the number is 2·638

log 2·638 = 0·4213

$2{\cdot}638 \longrightarrow 26{\cdot}38$ means move the decimal *one* place to the right, ∴ put **1** in front of the log.
thus, log $26{\cdot}38 = $ **1·4213.**

Example 3. To find log 468200.
In standard form the number is $4{\cdot}682$
log $4{\cdot}682 = $ **0·6704**
$4{\cdot}682 \longrightarrow 468200$ means moving the decimal *five* places to the right, ∴ put **5** in front of the log.
thus, log $468200 = $ **5·6704.**

4.4. Now turn to 4.13 on page 42

Chapter 5

Stage 3

Multiplication and division involving numbers less than unity

So far we have multiplied and divided numbers greater than one. Let us now deal with numbers less than one. Incidentally, we cannot use logs to deal with negative numbers. In questions involving minus signs, the sign must be dealt with separately, logs may then be used on the numerical quantities themselves, e.g. in -3.62×-2.41, $- \times -$ makes $+$, then 3.62×2.41 can be determined by logs.

5.1. Method 1 (*for Method 2 see 5.7, page 67*)

In order to multiply and divide numbers less than one we must be able to find logs for them.

Consider the following table:

No.	Log
2000·	3·3010
200·	2·3010
20·	1·3010
2·	0·3010
0·2	
0·02	
0·002	

In the number column, each number is one-tenth of the one above it. In the log column, the decimal part of each log is the same; and the number before the decimal is one less than the one above it. If we separate the two parts of each log, and continue the column of logs according to this rule we should get:

No.	Log
2000·	$3 + 0.3010$
200·	$2 + 0.3010$
20·	$1 + 0.3010$
2·	$0 + 0.3010$
0·2	$-1 + 0.3010$
0·02	$-2 + 0.3010$
0·002	$-3 + 0.3010$
	etc.

i.e. the decimal part stays the same and the number in front of the decimal becomes negative.

Thus, log of 0·2 $= -1 + 0.3010 = -0.6990$

and   log 0·02 $= -2 + 0.3010 = -1.6990$, etc.

But   log 2·0 $= 0.3010$

in other words we should need a new set of tables for numbers less than 1, unless we were prepared to do a subtraction sum each time. Again, notice that, in this system log 0·2 $= -0.6990$ and, from earlier results, log 5 $= 0.6990$: which might well cause confusion.

In order to avoid these difficulties we adopt a rather unusual notation for the logs of numbers less than 1.

We write log 0·2 $= -1 + 0.3010$ in the form $\bar{1}.3010$ which we call 'bar one point 3010'

In this we have placed the minus sign over the top of the 1, this means that the minus applies to the 1 only and not to the part after the decimal.

Similarly, log 0·02 $= \bar{2}.3010$ (bar 2 point 3010) etc.

In the same way, since log 3 $= 0.4771$

$$\log 0.3 = \bar{1}.4771$$
$$\log 0.003 = \bar{3}.4771$$
$$\text{etc.}$$

5.11.

Note: to determine the number before the decimal in the log, proceed as we did for numbers greater than 10 (see Chapter 4, page 40 and page 46).

Put the number in standard form and find the log, then count up the number of places the decimal must move to the *left* to return to the original number. This gives the number before the decimal in the log.

Example 1. To find log 0·000862
In standard form the number is 8·62
log 8·62 = 0·9355
8·62 ⟶ 0·000862 means move the decimal *four* places to the left, ∴ put $\bar{4}$ in front of the decimal in the log,
thus: log 0·000862 = $\bar{4}$·9355

Example 2. To find log 0·4628
In standard form the number is 4·628
log 4·628 = 0·6653
4·628 ⟶ 0·4628 means move the decimal *one* place to the left,
∴ put $\bar{1}$ in front of the decimal in the log,
thus log 0·4628 = $\bar{1}$·6653

5.12. To find the antilog we reverse the process.

Example 1. Find x if log x = $\bar{4}$·5823
    Antilog of 0·5823 = 3·822 which is in standard form. The $\bar{4}$ in front of the decimal in the log means move the decimal point in 3·822 *four* places to the left ∴ antilog $\bar{4}$·5823 = 0·0003822
∴ x = 0·0003822

Example 2. Find the antilog of $\bar{2}$·6868
Antilog of 0·6868 = 4·862 which is in standard form. The $\bar{2}$ in front of the decimal in the log means move the decimal point in 4·862 *two* places to the left.
∴ antilog $\bar{2}$·6868 = 0·04862

5.13. Examples 15a—Method 1

(1) Complete the following table:

	No.	Log
a	0·0808	
b	0·5623	
c	0·00423	
d		$\bar{6}$·5852
e		$\bar{1}$·2738
f		$\bar{2}$·9542

(2) $\log x = \bar{1}$·6754. Find x

(3) Find the log of 0·08787

(4) If x is the log of 0·9542, find x

(5) Find y if $\log y = \bar{1}$·6954

(6) Complete the following:

	No.	Log
a	0·5654	
b	5·732	
c	0·00852	
d	17·36	
e		$\bar{5}$·2243
f		3·7821
g		$\bar{1}$·9583
h		5·6724

(7) Find the logs of (a) 82·94, (b) 0·9537, (c) 0·08098, (d) 0·8673, (e) 1·562

(8) Find the antilogs of (a) $\bar{1}$·3456, (b) $\bar{2}$·9581, (c) 2·9031, (d) $\bar{2}$·4771, (e) 0·8868

(9) Find the numbers which have the following logs:
(a) $\bar{2}$·5434, (b) $\bar{1}$·8624, (c) 1·4838, (d) 2·1951, (e) $\bar{1}$·2641

(10) Find the logs of (a) 86·31, (b) 0·3542, (c) 0·08219, (d) 1·731, (e) 0·01

5.14. Examples 15b—Method 2

(1) Complete the following table:

	No.	Log
a	0·0808	
b	0·5623	
c	0·00423	
d		$\bar{6}$·5852
e		$\bar{1}$·2738
f		$\bar{2}$·9542

(2) $\log x = \bar{1}$·6754. Find x

(3) Find the log of 0·08787

(4) If 0·9542 $= 10^x$, find x

(5) If $10^{\bar{1}\cdot6954} = y$, find y

(6) Complete the following:

	No.	Log
a	0·5654	
b	5·732	
c	0·00852	
d	17·36	
e		$\bar{5}$·2243
f		3·7821
g		$\bar{1}$·9583
h		5·6724

(7) Find the logs of 82·94, 0·9537, 0·08098, 0·8673, 1·562.

(8) Find the antilogs of $\bar{1}$·3456, $\bar{2}$·9581, 2·9031, $\bar{2}$·4771, 0·8868.

(9) Find the value of $10^{\bar{2}\cdot5434}$, $10^{\bar{1}\cdot8624}$, $10^{1\cdot4838}$ $10^{2\cdot1951}$, $10^{\bar{1}\cdot2641}$

(10) Find x in each of the following,

$$10^x = 86\cdot31 \qquad 10^x = 0\cdot3542 \qquad 10^x = 0\cdot08219$$
$$10^x = 1\cdot731 \qquad 10^x = 0\cdot01$$

5.2. Addition of the logs

In order to be able to use these logs of numbers less than unity, we must know how to add and subtract them. These processes should be practised first before the logs are used in calculations.

5.21. Addition

Starting with the type of problems we have already done, let us consider as many different variations as possible.

$$
\begin{array}{lll}
\text{(a)} & 2{\cdot}6020 \quad \text{is equivalent to} & +2 + 0{\cdot}6020 \\
& 1{\cdot}1281 & +1 + 0{\cdot}1281 \\ \hline
& & +3 + 0{\cdot}7301
\end{array}
$$

$$
\begin{array}{lll}
\therefore\ & 2{\cdot}6020 \longrightarrow & +2 + 0{\cdot}6020 \\
& 1{\cdot}1281 \longrightarrow & +1 + 0{\cdot}1281 \\ \hline
& 3{\cdot}7301 \longleftarrow & +3 + 0{\cdot}7301
\end{array}
$$

$$
\begin{array}{lll}
\text{(b)} & 2{\cdot}6020 \longrightarrow & +2 + 0{\cdot}6020 \\
& \bar{1}{\cdot}1281 \longrightarrow & -1 + 0{\cdot}1281 \\ \hline
& 1{\cdot}7301 \longleftarrow & 1 + 0{\cdot}7301
\end{array}
$$

$$
\begin{array}{lll}
\text{(c)} & \bar{2}{\cdot}6020 \longrightarrow & -2 + 0{\cdot}6020 \\
& 1{\cdot}1281 \longrightarrow & +1 + 0{\cdot}1281 \\ \hline
& \bar{1}{\cdot}7301 \longleftarrow & -1 + 0{\cdot}7301
\end{array}
$$

$$
\begin{array}{lll}
\text{(d)} & \bar{2}{\cdot}6020 \longrightarrow & -2 + 0{\cdot}6020 \\
& \bar{1}{\cdot}1281 \longrightarrow & -1 + 0{\cdot}1281 \\ \hline
& \bar{3}{\cdot}7301 \longleftarrow & -3 + 0{\cdot}7301
\end{array}
$$

So far the two decimal parts have not added up to more than 1.

$$
\begin{array}{lll}
\text{(e)} & 2{\cdot}6020 \longrightarrow & +2 + 0{\cdot}6020 \\
& 1{\cdot}7281 \longrightarrow & +1 + 0{\cdot}7281 \\ \hline
& 4{\cdot}3301 \longleftarrow & 3 + 1{\cdot}3301
\end{array}
$$

$$
\begin{array}{lll}
\text{(f)} & \bar{2}{\cdot}6020 \longrightarrow & -2 + 0{\cdot}6020 \\
& 1{\cdot}7281 \longrightarrow & +1 + 0{\cdot}7281 \\ \hline
& 0{\cdot}3301 \longleftarrow & -1 + 1{\cdot}3301
\end{array}
$$

$$
\begin{array}{lll}
\text{(g)} & 2{\cdot}6020 \longrightarrow & +2 + 0{\cdot}6020 \\
& \bar{1}{\cdot}7281 \longrightarrow & -1 + 0{\cdot}7281 \\ \hline
& 2{\cdot}3301 \longleftarrow & 1 + 1{\cdot}3301
\end{array}
$$

(h) $\bar{2}\cdot6020$ $\longrightarrow$ $-2 + 0\cdot6020$

$\bar{1}\cdot7281$ $\longrightarrow$ $-1 + 0\cdot7281$

$2\cdot3301$ $\longleftarrow$ $-3 + 1\cdot3301$

This process of separating into two parts and then recombining, should be dropped as soon as possible, so that the whole operation can be done mentally as in addition of positive quantities.

Thus $\left.\begin{array}{l}\bar{2}\cdot6020 \\ \bar{1}\cdot7281\end{array}\right\}$ Add

$\bar{2}\cdot3301$

5.22. Examples 16

(1) $3\cdot1525$
$1\cdot2838$

(2) $1\cdot4515$
$0\cdot2535$

(3) $0\cdot6424$
$4\cdot1525$

(4) $\bar{4}\cdot5525$
$1\cdot2828$

(5) $\bar{3}\cdot1761$
$2\cdot5824$

(6) $\bar{1}\cdot4525$
$2\cdot3838$

(7) $3\cdot1654$
$\bar{1}\cdot2525$

(8) $4\cdot7818$
$\bar{2}\cdot1515$

(9) $2\cdot3828$
$\bar{2}\cdot1849$

(10) $\bar{2}\cdot5793$
$\bar{1}\cdot4141$

(11) $\bar{3}\cdot7218$
$\bar{3}\cdot1195$

(12) $\bar{1}\cdot2280$
$\bar{2}\cdot3215$

(13) $2\cdot6161$
$1\cdot8282$

(14) $5\cdot6789$
$1\cdot4415$

(15) $1\cdot7878$
$0\cdot9542$

(16) $2\cdot5543$
$\bar{1}\cdot7821$

(17) $3\cdot5617$
$\bar{3}\cdot9592$

(18) $4\cdot8841$
$\bar{2}\cdot7171$

(19) $1\cdot5119$
$\bar{2}\cdot8815$

(20) $2\cdot3475$
$\bar{4}\cdot9981$

(21) $0\cdot7878$
$\bar{1}\cdot9683$

(22) $\bar{1}\cdot8454$
$5\cdot3131$

(23) $\bar{2}\cdot9191$
$\bar{1}\cdot6868$

(24) $\bar{2}\cdot9981$
$\bar{3}\cdot9451$

(25) $6\cdot1434$
$\bar{7}\cdot9828$

(26) $\bar{1}\cdot7931$
$\bar{2}\cdot5524$

(27) $\bar{2}\cdot3131$
$1\cdot9842$

(28) $1\cdot6828$
$\bar{2}\cdot9137$

(29) $\bar{3}\cdot9828$
$\bar{2}\cdot2818$

(30) $0\cdot4954$
$\bar{1}\cdot8282$

5.3. Application to multiplication

Now let us make use of this in multiplication.

5.31. Worked examples

(1) 3.606×0.9192
   $= 3.31$

   cf. type (g) above

No.	Log	
3.606 0.9192	0.5570 $\bar{1}$.9634	}Add
3.314 ←—	0.5204	

(2) 0.006532×0.01092
   $= 0.0000713$

   cf. type (d) above

No.	Log
0.006532 0.01092	$\bar{3}$.8150 $\bar{2}$.0382
0.00007132 ←—	5.8532

(3) 0.0952×0.8371
   $= 0.0797$

   cf. type (h) above

No.	Log
0.0952 0.8371	$\bar{2}$.9786 $\bar{1}$.9228
0.07969 ←—	$\bar{2}$.9014

5.32. Examples 17

(1) 15.28×3.94 (2) 46.78×0.02031
(3) 0.04626×14.22 (4) 0.01932×0.2676
(5) 82.41×39.38 (6) 76.34×0.0084
(7) 0.0953×77.26 (8) 0.0854×0.009731
(9) 46.3×0.982 (10) 0.9631×0.9822
(11) $[0.9616]^2$ (12) $3.78 \times 0.7491 \times 0.886$

5.33. Practical applications

(1) Find the volume, in cubic metres, of a cylinder of height
   6.5 cm and radius 27 cm

$$6.5 \text{ cm} = 0.065 \text{ m}$$
$$27 \text{ cm} = 0.27 \text{ m}$$

Volume of cylinder $= \pi r^2 h$ $\pi = 3\cdot142$
$\therefore$ Volume of given cylinder $= 3\cdot142 \times (\cdot27)^2 \times 0\cdot065$ m³
$= 3\cdot142 \times 0\cdot27 \times 0\cdot27 \times 0\cdot065$ m³
$= 0\cdot0149$ m³

No.	Log
3·142	0·4972
0·27	$\bar{1}$·4314
0·27	$\bar{1}$·4314
0·065	$\bar{2}$·8129
0·01489	$\bar{2}$·1729

(2) Find the length of AB in the triangle ABC.

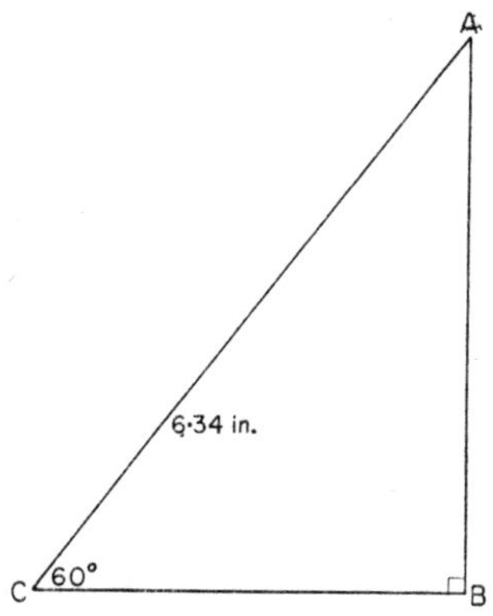

$$\sin C = \frac{AB}{AC} \qquad \therefore \sin 60° = \frac{AB}{6\cdot34}$$

$\therefore AB = 6\cdot34 \sin 60°$
$\quad = 6\cdot34 \times 0\cdot8660$
$\quad = 5\cdot49$ in.

No.	Log
6·34	0·8021
sin 60°	$\bar{1}$·9375
5·491 $\leftarrow$	0·7396

(3) If the increase in volume of a solid is given by $L \times c \times t$,
find this increase when $L = 3624$, $c = 0\cdot000028$, and
$t = 320$.

Increase
$$= 3624 \times 0.000028 \times 320$$
$$= 32.5$$

No.	Log
3624	3.5592
0.000028	$\bar{5}$.4472
320	2.5051
32.47	1.5115

5.34. Examples 18

(1) Find the area, in sq. cm, of the curved surface of a cylinder of radius 55 mm and height 3·5 mm.

(2) A solid consists of a cylinder with a hemisphere on one end. Both parts have a radius of 93 mm, and the height of the cylinder is 6 cm. Find the volume of the solid in cu. cm.

(3) Find the simple interest on £682 10s. 0d. for 3 months at 2·5%.

(4) Find the volume of a circular cone of radius 0·8 cm and height 0·7 cm. (Volume of a cone $= \frac{1}{3}$ base area $\times$ height).

(5) If the increase in length of a solid is given by $l = L \times c \times t$, find l when $L = 248$, $c = 0.0000218$, and $t = 45$.

(6) The formula $s = k + \dfrac{8h^2}{3k}$ gives the length (s) of a chain where $k =$ span and $h =$ sag. Find s when $k = 1.5$ and $h = 0.77$.

(7) Find the area between two concentric circles of radii 1·32 in. and 0·85 in.

(8) 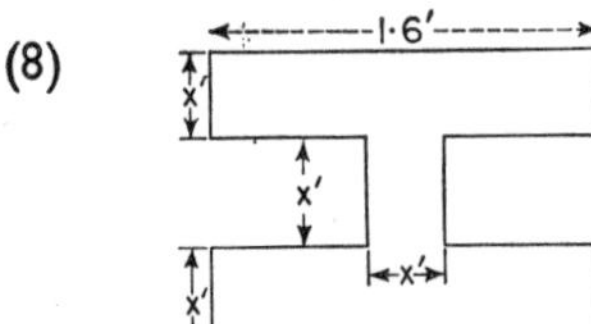

The diagram shows the cross-section of a solid which is 15 ft long. Prove that the volume is $= 15x^2 + 48x$, and find the volume when $x = 0.92$.

(9) Find the volume of a wire of circular cross-section, if it is half-a-mile long and has a radius of 0·228 in. (Answer in cubic feet.)

(10) If $s = ut + \frac{1}{2}$ ft^2, find s when $u = 40$, $t = 13.25$, and $f = 0.88$.

5.4. Subtraction of the logs

Two distinct methods of subtraction of ordinary numbers are in common use in schools.

Thus 362—
195
—
167

Method (1).   12 minus 5 $= 7$ or $10 - 5 + 2 = 7$
$\therefore$ *Add* one on to the 9, making 10
16 minus 10 $= 6$ or $10 - 10 + 6 = 6$
Add one on to the 1 making 2
3 minus 2 $= 1$

Method (2)   12 minus 5 $= 7$
$\therefore$ *Subtract* 1 from the 6 making 5
15 minus 9 $= 6$
Subtract 1 from the 3 making 2
2 minus 1 $= 1$

It was suggested, in the addition of logs of numbers less than one, that the intermediate step (of separating the whole number and the decimal parts of the logs), should be discontinued as soon as possible. In subtraction, especially by Method (1) it is better to miss out the intermediate step of separating the two parts, if at all possible.

Again, let us consider as many different cases of subtraction as possible, in order of increasing difficulty, taking first those which do not involve any 'carry over' across the decimal point.

5.41.

(a) 2·6820—
1·1241
—
1·5579

Method (i)
10 minus 1 $= 9$
Add 1 to the 4 making 5

12 minus 5 $= 7$
Add 1 to the 2 making 3

8 minus 3 $= 5$
6 minus 1 $= 5$
Decimal point (·)
2 minus 1 $= 1$

Method (ii)
10 minus 1 $= 9$
Subtract 1 from the 2 making 1
11 minus 4 $= 7$
Subtract 1 from the 8 making 7
7 minus 2 $= 5$
6 minus 1 $= 5$
Decimal point (·)
2 minus 1 $= 1$

(b) 2·6820   Methods (i) and (ii) as before up to decimal point
    4·1241 $2 - 4 = -2 = \bar{2}$
    $\overline{2}$·5579

(c) $\bar{2}$·6820   As in (a) up to decimal point
    1·1241 $\bar{2} - 1 = -2 - 1 = -3 = \bar{3}$
    $\bar{3}$·5579

(d) 2·6820   As in (a) up to decimal point
    $\bar{1}$·1241 $2 - \bar{1} = 2 - (-1) = 2 + 1 = 3$
    3·5579

(e) $\bar{2}$·6820   As in (a) up to decimal point
    $\bar{1}$·1241 $\bar{2} - \bar{1} = -2 - (-1) = -2 + 1 = -1 = \bar{1}$
    $\bar{1}$·5579

(f) $\bar{2}$·6820   As in (a) up to decimal point
    $\bar{4}$·1241 $\bar{2} - \bar{4} = -2 - (-4) = -2 + 4 = 2$
    2·5579

For practice in these simple types, see Examples 19, Nos. 1–18.

5.42.

The following cases are more difficult, in that there is a 'carry over' across the decimal point.

(g) 2·6820   *Method (i)*   *Method (ii)*
    1·9241 $10 - 1 = 9$ $10 - 1 = 9$
    0·7579   Add 1 to the 4 making 5   Subtract 1 from 2 making 1
              $12 - 5 = 7$ $11 - 4 = 7$
              Add 1 to the 2 making 3   Subtract 1 from 8 making 7
              $8 - 3 = 5$ $7 - 2 = 5$
              $16 - 9 = 7$ $16 - 9 = 7$
              Decimal point (·)   Decimal point (·)
              Add 1 to the 1   Subtract 1 from 2
              making 2   making 1
              $2 - 2 = 0$ $1 - 1 = 0$

(h) 2·6820
    3·9241
    ‾‾‾‾‾‾
    $\bar{2}$·7579

Method (i)	*Method (ii)*
As in (g) up to decimal point	As in (g) up to decimal point
Add 1 to the 3 giving 4	Subtract 1 from the 2 giving 1
2. $-$ 4 $= -2$	1 $-$ 3 $= -2$
$= \bar{2}$	$= \bar{2}$

(i) $\bar{2}$·6820
    3·9241
    ‾‾‾‾‾‾
    $\bar{6}$·7579

Method (i)	*Method (ii)*
As in (g) up to decimal point	As in (g) up to decimal point
Add 1 to 3 giving 4	Subtract 1 from $\bar{2}$
$\bar{2} - 4 = -2 - 4 = -6$	i.e. $-2 - 1$ giving -3
$\quad = \bar{6}$	i.e. $\bar{3}$
	then $-3 - 3 = -6$
	$\quad = \bar{6}$

(j) 2·6820
    $\bar{3}$·9241
    ‾‾‾‾‾‾
    4·7579

Method (i)	*Method (ii)*
As in (g) up to decimal point	As in (g) up to decimal point
Add 1 to $\bar{3}$, i.e. $-3 + 1$ giving -2 or $\bar{2}$	Subtract 1 from 2 giving 1
then	then $1 - (-3) = 1 + 3$
$+2 - \bar{2} = +2 - (-2)$	$\quad = 4$
$\quad = +2 + 2$	
$\quad = 4$	

(k) $\bar{1}$·6820
    $\bar{3}$·9241
    ‾‾‾‾‾‾
    $\bar{1}$·7579

Method (i)	*Method (ii)*
As in (g) up to decimal point	As in (g) up to decimal point
Add 1 to $\bar{3}$, i.e. $-3 + 1$ giving $-2 = \bar{2}$	Subtract 1 from $\bar{1}$, i.e. $-1 - 1 = -2$
then	then $-2 - (-3) =$
$-1 - (\bar{2}) = -1 - (-2)$	$-2 + 3 = 1$
$\quad = -1 + 2$	
$\quad = 1$	

(I)   6820   *Method (i)*   *Method (ii)*
       $\bar{1}$·9241   As in (g) up to decimal   As in (g) up to decimal
       $\overline{4\cdot7579}$ point   point
                          Add I to $\bar{1}$,   Subtract I from $\bar{4}$,
                          i.e. $-I + I = 0$ i.e. $-4 - I = -5$
                          then $-4 - 0 = -4$ then
                                                        $-5 - (-I) = -5 + I$
                                                        $= -4 = \bar{4}$

For types (g) to (I) see Examples 19, Nos. 19–36

5.43. Examples 19

Subtract the following logs.

(I) 3·6245	(2) 1·6542	(3) 2·7815
2·4195	0·5526	1·6431
(4) 1·7153	(5) 0·7532	(6) 4·3852
3·2415	1·6161	5·1431
(7) $\bar{3}$·8243	(8) $\bar{2}$·4924	(9) $\bar{4}$·7672
1·1415	0·3151	3·1688
(10) 4·5846	(II) 5·6262	(12) 0·5624
$\bar{1}$·1931	$\bar{2}$·3131	$\bar{3}$·1921
(13) $\bar{4}$·8526	(14) $\bar{4}$·6473	(15) $\bar{2}$·5624
$\bar{2}$·3432	$\bar{1}$·5132	$\bar{1}$·1456
(16) $\bar{1}$·6954	(17) $\bar{2}$·9542	(18) $\bar{6}$·7171
$\bar{3}$·1582	$\bar{6}$·3838	$\bar{8}$·6325
(19) 4·5842	(20) 3·6871	(21) 5·8283
2·9316	2·9191	1·9982
(22) 3·7963	(23) 1·6464	(24) 0·6824
5·8215	5·7763	3·8828
(25) $\bar{2}$·5445	(26) $\bar{1}$·8282	(27) $\bar{4}$·6388
4·6243	4·9198	4·8836
(28) 1·1914	(29) 2·1066	(30) 0·8864
$\bar{2}$·2688	$\bar{3}$·1492	$\bar{1}$·9737

(31) $\bar{1}$·2730
    $\bar{4}$·8800

(32) $\bar{2}$·7969
    $\bar{3}$·9697

(33) $\bar{6}$·1860
    $\bar{9}$·3141

(34) $\bar{6}$·7828
    $\bar{2}$·9798

(35) $\bar{2}$·3172
    $\bar{1}$·8293

(36) $\bar{4}$·7628
    $\bar{2}$·8195

5.44. Examples 20

Subtract the following logs.

(1) $\bar{1}$·6868
   2·3979

(2) $\bar{3}$·8295
   $\bar{4}$·9541

(3) 1·2838
   $\bar{1}$·9199

(4) 1·6828
   2·9341

(5) 2·8686
   $\bar{2}$·8686

(6) $\bar{2}$·3824
   0·4971

(7) $\bar{5}$·1828
   $\bar{2}$·0837

(8) $\bar{3}$·2424
   $\bar{3}$·1542

(9) 2·6828
   $\bar{3}$·8682

(10) 3·7824
    $\bar{3}$·6868

5.5. Application to division

Now let us make use of this in division.

5.51. Worked examples (involving the subtraction of logs)

(1) $0.8254 \div 2.641$
   (type c)
   $= 0.313$

No.	Log	
0·8254	$\bar{1}$·9167	⎫
2·641	0·4218	⎬ Subtract
0·3125 ←	— $\bar{1}$·4949	

(2) $0.8641 \div 0.0941$
   (type k)
   $= 9.18$

No.	Log	
0·8641	$\bar{1}$·9366	⎫
0·0941	$\bar{2}$·9736	⎬ Subtract
9·183 ←	— 0·9630	

(3) $6\cdot824 \div 0\cdot0831$
    $= 82\cdot1$

No.	Log	
6·824	0·8341	⎫
0·0831	$\bar{2}$·9196	⎬ Subtract
82·13 ←—	1·9145	

(4) $0\cdot08245 \div 0\cdot1561$
    $= 0\cdot528$

No.	Log	
0·08245	$\bar{2}$·9162	⎫
0·1561	$\bar{1}$·1934	⎬ Subtract
0·5282 ←—	$\bar{1}$·7228	

(5) $12\cdot96 \div 159\cdot6$
    $= 0\cdot0812$

No.	Log	
12·96	1·1127	⎫
159·6	2·2031	⎬ Subtract
0·08121 ←—	$\bar{2}$·9096	

5.52. Examples 21

(1) $0\cdot9531 \div 0\cdot862$ (2) $46\cdot37 \div 0\cdot1564$

(3) $38\cdot77 \div 2\cdot56$ (4) $0\cdot8261 \div 37\cdot88$

(5) $\dfrac{0\cdot9821}{0\cdot7862}$ (6) $\dfrac{11\cdot2}{185\cdot6}$

(7) $\dfrac{0\cdot8641}{0\cdot9954}$ (8) $\dfrac{0\cdot08809}{0\cdot6954}$

(9) $\dfrac{11\cdot68}{0\cdot0868}$ (10) $0\cdot6475 \div 9\cdot2$

(11) $\dfrac{36\cdot4 \times 0\cdot98}{1\cdot686}$ (12) $\dfrac{56\cdot7 \times 0\cdot36 \times 0\cdot28}{0\cdot9541}$

5.53. Examples 22

(1) Calculate sin A in the triangle ABC.

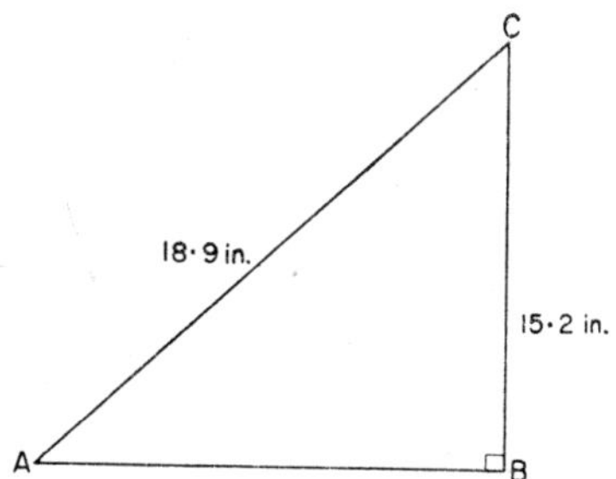

(2) I cu. ft of water weighs 62·43 lb, I in. $= 2\cdot540$ cm, and I kg $= 2\cdot205$ lb. Use these results to show that the density of water is I g/cm^3.

(3) I litre of hydrogen at N.T.P. weighs 0·0889 g. Under these conditions find (a) the weight of 310 cm^3 of hydrogen, (b) the volume occupied by 0·05 g of the gas.

(4) The density of air at N.T.P. $= 0\cdot00129$ g/cm^3. Find the volume of 0·085 g at N.T.P.

(5) I joule $= 0\cdot2389$ calories, how many joules in 2698 calories? Give your answer in the form $A \times 10^n$, where n is an integer and A is a number between I and I0.

5.6. Miscellaneous examples

5.61. Examples 23

(1) $6\cdot629 \times 0\cdot382$ (2) $0\cdot981 \div 6\cdot711$ (3) $\dfrac{3\cdot62}{0\cdot994}$

(4) $0\cdot099 \times 0\cdot3124$ (5) $17\cdot79 \times 142\cdot1$ (6) $0\cdot3939 \times 0\cdot4882$

(7) $\dfrac{147\cdot3}{1894200}$ (8) $\dfrac{3\cdot772 \times 1\cdot966}{0\cdot385}$ (9) $0\cdot077 \times 0\cdot0954$

(10) $\dfrac{3\cdot712}{0\cdot0883}$ (11) $\dfrac{3\cdot619 \times 147\cdot3}{13\cdot78 \times 8492}$ (12) $\dfrac{41\cdot72 \times 0\cdot000381}{78\cdot66}$

(13) $\dfrac{0\cdot08981}{0\cdot9878}$ (14) $\dfrac{7\cdot606 \times 0\cdot04004}{1\cdot003 \times 467}$ (15) $\dfrac{8\cdot882 \times 14\cdot7}{3\cdot64 \times 1\cdot19}$

(16) $\dfrac{13\cdot6 - 12\cdot9}{13\cdot6 + 12\cdot9}$ (17) $\dfrac{8\cdot867 \times 0\cdot000971}{361\cdot8}$ (18) $\dfrac{14\cdot9}{12\cdot7 \times 0\cdot08016}$

(19) $11\cdot79 \div 7\cdot881$ (20) $0\cdot88 \times 0\cdot79 \div 0\cdot976$

5.62. Examples 24 (practical problems)

(1) Use the Sine rule to find AB in the triangle ABC.

$$\left(\frac{a}{\sin A} = \frac{b}{\sin B} = \frac{c}{\sin C}\right)$$

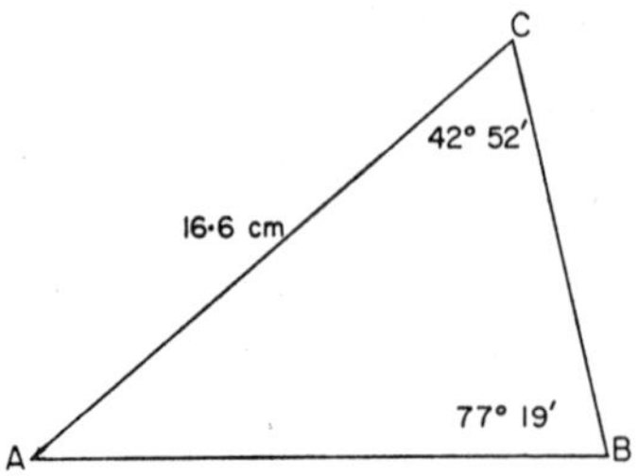

(2) The resistance of a wire, of circular cross-section, is given by the formula $R = \dfrac{k.l}{d^2}$, where l = length and d = diameter of cross-section.
If $R = 0\cdot04$ when $l = 60$ cm and $d = 0\cdot052$ cm, find k, and hence find R when $l = 253$ cm and $d = 0\cdot085$ cm.

(3) The vertical distance fallen by a particle is given by the formula $s = \frac{1}{2}gt^2$. If $g = 32\cdot2$ and $t = 0\cdot53$ find s.

(4) From the gas laws, $\dfrac{p_1 v_1}{t_1} = \dfrac{p_2 v_2.}{t_2}$. Find v_2 if $p_1 = 760$, $v_1 = 0\cdot8$, $t_1 = 273$, $p_2 = 795$, and $t_2 = 290$.

(5) Find the area of curved surface of a cylindrical wire of length 50 cm and radius 0·08 cm. What length of this wire would have an area of curved surface = 1 sq. cm?

(6) What length of wire can be made from a rectangular block of metal 4·2 cm by 8·3 cm by 7·6 cm if the wire is to have a cross-sectional area of 0·0052 sq. cm?

(7) The density of air at N.T.P. $= 0.00129$ g/cm^3. Find the volume occupied by 5·6 g of air (a) at N.T.P. and (b) at a pressure of 780 mm and a temperature of 14°C.

(8) If 1 litre of hydrogen weighs 0·0889 g, find
    (a) the weight, in grammes, of 65 cm^3.
    (b) the weight in lb of 1 cu. ft, given that 1 in. $= 2.540$ cm, and 1 lb $= 453.6$ g.

(9) The area of the surface of a sphere $= 4\pi r^2$.
    Find the area of the surface of a spherical bubble of radius 0·35 in.

(10) The angle of banking of a curved track is given by $\tan A = \dfrac{v^2}{rg}$, where v is in ft/sec, r is in feet, and g is in ft/sec^2. Find $\tan A$ if $v = 45$ m.p.h., $r = 500$ ft, and $g = 32.2$ ft/sec^2.

———

Now turn to Chapter 6 on page 69.

5.7. Method 2

Since $\log 2 = 0.3010$ we have
$$2 = 10^{0.3010}$$

We have already shown that
$$200 = 100 \times 2 = 10^2 \times 10^{0.3010}$$
$$= 10^{2.3010}$$
$$20 = 10 \times 2 = 10^1 \times 10^{0.3010}$$
$$= 10^{1.3010}$$
$$\text{and} \quad 2 = 10^{0.3010}$$

But
$$0.2 = \frac{2}{10} = \frac{1}{10} \times 2 = 10^{-1} \times 2$$
$$= 10^{-1} \times 10^{0.3010} = 10^{-1+0.3010}$$

$$0.02 = \frac{2}{100} = \frac{1}{100} \times 2 = \frac{1}{10^2} \times 2$$
$$= 10^{-2} \times 2 = 10^{-2} \times 10^{0.3010}$$
$$= 10^{-2+0.3010}$$

F

$$0.002 = \frac{2}{1000} = \frac{1}{10^3} \times 2 = 10^{-3} \times 10^{0.3010}$$
$$= 10^{-3+0.3010}$$
$$0.2 \quad = 10^{-1+0.3010} = 10^{-0.6990}$$
$$0.02 \quad = 10^{-2+0.3010} = 10^{-1.6990}$$
$$0.002 = 10^{-3+0.3010} = 10^{-2.6990}$$
$$\therefore \log 0.2 \quad = -0.6990$$
$$\log 0.02 \quad = -1.6990$$
$$\text{and } \log 0.002 = -2.6990 \text{ etc.}$$
$$\text{But } \log \quad 2 = 0.3010$$
$$\log \quad 20 = 1.3010$$
$$\log \quad 200 = 2.3010$$

In other words, for numbers >1, the logs of 2, 20, 200, 2000, etc., all have 3010 after the decimal. But for numbers <1, the logs of 0.2, 0.02, 0.002, etc. all have 6990 after the decimal.

This would mean a different set of tables for numbers less than 1.

To avoid this difficulty, instead of writing $-1 + 0.3010$ as -0.6990, we write $\bar{1}.3010$, putting the $-$ sign above the one, to indicate that only the 1 is negative.

Again, instead of $-2 + 0.3010$, we write $\bar{2}.3010$, and call this 'bar 2 point 3010'

$\therefore$

No.	Log
200	2.3010
20	1.3010
2	0.3010
0.2	$\bar{1}$.3010
0.02	$\bar{2}$.3010
0.002	$\bar{3}$.3010
0.0002	$\bar{4}$.3010

5.8. Now turn to 5.11, on page 51.

Stage 4

Powers and roots—
methods 1 and 2 combined

6.1. Powers: (a) Numbers greater than 1

Suppose we want to calculate $(3{\cdot}56)^4$
$(3{\cdot}56)^4 = 3{\cdot}56 \times 3{\cdot}56 \times 3{\cdot}56 \times 3{\cdot}56$

$\therefore$ we could calculate it as follows

$(3{\cdot}56)^4 = 161.$

No.	Log	
3·56	0·5514	
3·56	0·5514	
3·56	0·5514	Add
3·56	0·5514	
160·5	2·2056	

But $0{\cdot}5514 + 0{\cdot}5514 + 0{\cdot}5514 + 0{\cdot}5514$
$\qquad = 0{\cdot}5514 \times 4$

$\therefore$ we could rewrite the table of logs thus:

No.	Log	
3·56	0·5514 4	Multiply
(3·56⁴)	2·2056	

Logarithms

Clearly when high powers are required this latter method is much quicker.

$\therefore$ If we want to find the nth power of a number, we find the log, multiply the log by n, and then find the antilog.

Example
$(4 \cdot 31)^7$

No.	Log	
4·31	0·6345	
	7	} Multiply
27640·	4·4415	

$= 27600.$

Thus in general we have $r^n = r \times r \times r \dots n$ times

$\therefore \log r^n = \log r + \log r + \log r \dots n$ times

$\qquad = n \cdot \log r.$

6.11. Examples 25

1. $(62 \cdot 9)^3$ 2. $(14 \cdot 7)^5$ 3. $(1 \cdot 82)^{11}$
4. $(15 \cdot 63)^4$ 5. $(9 \cdot 81)^7$

6.2. Powers: (b) Numbers less than 1

Suppose we want to calculate $(0 \cdot 31)^4$,

By the first method:

No.	Log	
0·31	$\bar{1}$·4914	
0·31	$\bar{1}$·4914	
0·31	$\bar{1}$·4914	} Add
0·31	$\bar{1}$·4914	
0·009239	$\bar{3}$·9656	

$= 0 \cdot 00924$

By the second method:

No.	Log	
0·31	$\bar{1}$·4914	
	4	} Multiply
0·009239	$\bar{3}$·9656	

$= 0 \cdot 00924$

$$\text{Note: } \overline{1}\cdot4914 \times 4 = (-1 + 0\cdot4914) \times 4$$
$$= -4 + 1\cdot9656$$
$$= \overline{3}\cdot9656$$

Some students may find the first method easier, but it becomes cumbersome for high powers. The second method is therefore considered in greater detail.

6.21.

We first consider the manipulation of the logs and then apply the method to specific problems.

(a)

$\overline{1}\cdot2243$ $\rightarrow$	$-1 + 0\cdot2243$
$\times 3$ $\rightarrow$	$\times 3$
$\overline{3}\cdot6729$ $\leftarrow$	$-3 + 0\cdot6729$

Multiply

(b)

$\overline{1}\cdot4243$ $\rightarrow$	$-1 + 0\cdot4243$
$\times 3$	$\times 3$
$\overline{2}\cdot2729$ $\leftarrow$	$-3 + 1\cdot2729 \ (= -3 + 1 + 0\cdot2729 = -2 + 0\cdot2729)$

(c)

$\overline{3}\cdot4243$ $\rightarrow$	$-3 + 0\cdot4243$
$\times 3$	$\times 3$
$\overline{8}\cdot2729$ $\leftarrow$	$-9 + 1\cdot2729$

6.22. Worked examples

(1) $(0\cdot0718)^4$

No.	Log
$0\cdot0718$	$\overline{2}\cdot8561 \rightarrow -2 + 0\cdot8561$
	$\times 4 \qquad\qquad \times 4$
$0\cdot00002657$	$\overline{5}\cdot4244 \leftarrow -8 + 3\cdot4244$

$= 0\cdot0000266$

(2) $(0.00156)^3$

No.	Log	
0.00156	$\bar{3}.1931$ $\times\ 3$	$-3 + 0.1931$ $\times\ 3$
0.000000003796	$\bar{9}.5793$	$-9 + 0.5793$

$= 0.00000000380$

6.23. Examples 26

1. $(0.38)^2$ 2. $(0.57)^3$ 3. $(0.096)^4$
4. $(2.009)^2$ 5. $(0.0032)^3$ 6. $(0.82)^3$
7. $(0.19)^4$ 8. $(0.38)^3 + (0.49)^3$ 9. $(3.62)^2 + (0.91)^2$
10. $(0.38)^2 \times 4.093$

6.3. Roots: (a) Numbers greater than 1

In stage 3.1 (e), page 26, we had $r^{1/2} \times r^{1/2} = r$, i.e. $r^{1/2}$ multiplied by itself $= r$

$\therefore r^{1/2} = \sqrt{r}$

$\therefore 8 = 64^{1/2} = \sqrt{64}, \quad 7 = 49^{1/2} = \sqrt{49}$, etc.

Also, since $8 \times 8 = 64$,

$\log 8 + \log 8 = \log 64$,

$\therefore 2 \log 8 = \log 64$,

$\therefore \log 8 = \tfrac{1}{2} \log 64$.

Similarly $\log 7 = \tfrac{1}{2} \log 49$,

These can be checked from the tables thus,

$\log\ \ 8 = 0.9031$

$\log\ 64 = 1.8062$

$\log\ \ 7 = 0.8451$

$\log\ 49 = 1.6902$

$\therefore \log \sqrt{r} = \log r^{1/2} = \tfrac{1}{2} \log r$

This agrees with the rule we had for powers, viz. $\log r^n = n \log r$

If we put $n = \tfrac{1}{2}$ we get $\log r^{1/2} = \tfrac{1}{2} \log r$

∴ To find a square root, find the log, multiply by $\frac{1}{2}$ (or divide by 2) and then find the antilog.

Thus:
$\sqrt{4 \cdot 262}$
$= 2 \cdot 07$

	No.	Log	
	4·262	0·6296	÷ 2
$(\sqrt{4 \cdot 262})$	2·065	0·3148	

Similarly, $\sqrt[3]{r} = r^{1/3}$
∴ To find a cube root, find the log, multiply by $\frac{1}{3}$ (i.e. divide it by 3) and find the antilog.

Thus:
$\sqrt[3]{9 \cdot 185}$
$= 2 \cdot 09$

	No.	Log	
	9·185	0·9630	÷ 3
$(\sqrt[3]{9 \cdot 185})$	2·094	0·3210	

Similarly for the 4th, 5th, and other roots, $\log r^{1/n} = (1/n) \log r$

6.31. Examples 27

(1) $\sqrt{8 \cdot 967}$ (2) $\sqrt[3]{142 \cdot 3}$ (3) $(87 \cdot 6)^{1/3}$

(4) $(17 \cdot 69)^{1/4}$ (5) $\sqrt[5]{188 \cdot 2}$

6.4. Roots: (b) Numbers less than 1

To find $\sqrt{0 \cdot 008642}$ we find the log of $0 \cdot 008642$ and divide it by 2, then find the antilog.

But $\log 0 \cdot 008642 = \bar{3} \cdot 9366$

$$\text{and } \frac{\bar{3} \cdot 9366}{2} = \frac{-3 + 0 \cdot 9366}{2} = -1 \cdot 5 + 0 \cdot 4683$$

This leads to a negative decimal which we try to avoid in logs— as mentioned earlier. (5.1, page 49, and 5.7, page 67.)

∴ we arrange the division so as to give a whole negative number before a positive decimal.

6.41.

Let us consider an easier example first.

Suppose we want to divide $\bar{7}{\cdot}0000$ by 2. We can write this as $\dfrac{-7 + 0{\cdot}0000}{2}$. We want to arrange this so that the division will give a whole negative number and a positive decimal.

$\therefore$ we increase the -7 to the first figure which can be divided by 2, i.e. increase it to -8. In order to keep the original fraction the same value we must add 1 on to the $0{\cdot}0000$, thus:

$$\frac{-7 + 0{\cdot}0000}{2} = \frac{-8 + 1{\cdot}0000}{2}$$

Dividing this will give a negative number followed by a positive decimal, thus:

$$\frac{-8 + 1{\cdot}0000}{2} = -4 + 0{\cdot}5000 = \bar{4}{\cdot}5000$$

$$\therefore \frac{7{\cdot}0000}{2} = \bar{4}{\cdot}5000$$

Worked examples

Example 1

$$\frac{\bar{7}{\cdot}0000}{3} = \frac{-7 + 0{\cdot}0000}{3}$$

Increase the -7 until it can be divided by 3, i.e. increase it to -9.

$\therefore$ Add $+2$ to the decimal to keep the fraction at its original value, thus:

$$\frac{-7 + 0{\cdot}0000}{3} = \frac{-9 + 2{\cdot}0000}{3}$$

$$= -3 + 0{\cdot}6667 = \bar{3}{\cdot}6667$$

Example 2

$$\frac{\bar{3}{\cdot}5000}{2} = \frac{-3 + 0{\cdot}5000}{2} = \frac{-4 + 1{\cdot}5000}{2}$$

$$= -2 + 0{\cdot}7500 = \bar{2}{\cdot}7500$$

Example 3

$$\frac{\bar{4}\cdot 6823}{3} = \frac{-4 + 0\cdot 6823}{3} = \frac{-6 + 2\cdot 6823}{3}$$

$$= -2 + 0\cdot 8941 = \bar{2}\cdot 8941$$

Example 4

$$\frac{\bar{3}\cdot 9366}{2} = \frac{-3 + 0\cdot 9366}{2} = \frac{-4 + 1\cdot 9366}{2}$$

$$= -2 + 0\cdot 9683 = \bar{2}\cdot 9683$$

6.42. Examples 28

(1) $\dfrac{\bar{5}\cdot 0000}{3}$ (2) $\dfrac{\bar{2}\cdot 6000}{4}$ (3) $\dfrac{\bar{3}\cdot 5600}{4}$

(4) $\dfrac{\bar{2}\cdot 8643}{3}$ (5) $\dfrac{\bar{4}\cdot 2625}{3}$ (6) $\dfrac{\bar{1}\cdot 5648}{2}$

(7) $\dfrac{\bar{4}\cdot 8943}{3}$ (8) $\dfrac{\bar{5}\cdot 6068}{4}$ (9) $\dfrac{\bar{5}\cdot 6243}{5}$

(10) $\dfrac{\bar{8}\cdot 6732}{9}$

6.43.

Therefore we can now return to our original problem (in 6.4)

To find $\sqrt{0\cdot 008642}$

log of $0\cdot 008642 = \bar{3}\cdot 9366$

To find the square root we divide the log by 2, and then find the antilog.

$$\frac{\bar{3}\cdot 9366}{2} = \frac{-3 + 0\cdot 9366}{2} = \frac{-4 + 1\cdot 9366}{2}$$

$$= -2 + 0\cdot 9683 \text{ (from Worked example 4,}$$
$$\text{above)}$$

$$= \bar{2}\cdot 9683$$

Antilog of $\bar{2}\cdot 9683 = 0\cdot 09296$

$\therefore \sqrt{0\cdot 008642} = 0\cdot 0930$

We can now set out this in the usual table, thus:

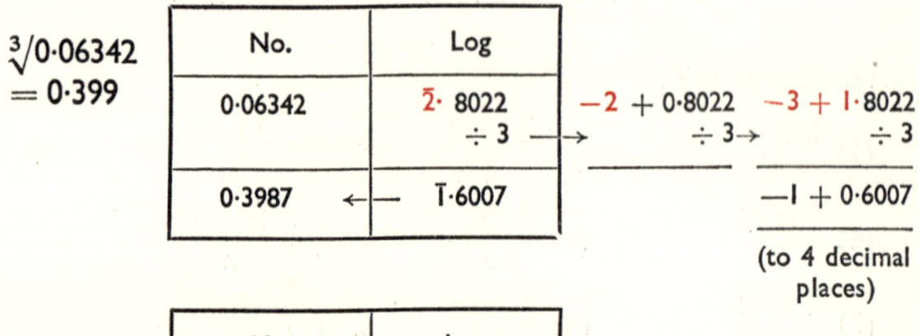

$\sqrt{0.008642}$
$= 0.0930$

No.	Log
0.008642	$\bar{3}\cdot9366$
	$\div\ 2$
0.09296 ←—	$\bar{2}\cdot9683$

$-3 + 0.9366 = -4 + 1.9366$
$\div\ 2 \qquad\qquad \div\ 2$
$\overline{\hphantom{xxxxxxx}}$
$-2 + 0.9683$

6.44. Further examples

$\sqrt[3]{0.06342}$
$= 0.399$

No.	Log
0.06342	$\bar{2}\cdot8022$
	$\div\ 3$ —→
0.3987 ←—	$\bar{1}\cdot6007$

$-2 + 0.8022 \quad -3 + 1.8022$
$\div\ 3→ \qquad\qquad \div\ 3$
$\overline{\hphantom{xxxxxxx}}$
$-1 + 0.6007$

(to 4 decimal places)

$\sqrt[4]{0.00007632}$
$= 0.0935$

No.	Log
0.00007632	$\bar{5}\cdot8826$
	$\div\ 4$
0.09348 ←—	$\bar{2}\cdot9707$

$-5 + 0.8826 \quad -8 + 3.8826$
$\div\ 4→ \qquad\qquad \div\ 4$
$\overline{\hphantom{xxxxxxx}}$
$-2 + 0.9707$

(to 4 decimal places)

6.45. Examples 29
1. $\sqrt{0.9563}$ 2. $\sqrt[3]{0.08283}$ 3. $\sqrt{0.009761}$
4. $\sqrt[4]{0.8263}$ 5. $\sqrt[5]{0.0007418}$ 6. $\sqrt{0.09908}$
7. $\sqrt[3]{0.01066}$ 8. $(0.08077)^{1/3}$ 9. $(0.6054)^{1/2}$
10. $(0.6676)^{1/4}$

6.5. More difficult cases

It was also established in Stage 1 §3.1 (e) that $a^{2/3} = \sqrt[3]{a^2}$
$a^{4/5} = \sqrt[5]{a^4}$ etc.

∴ To find $(3.682)^{2/3}$
$(3.682)^{2/3} = \sqrt[3]{3.682^2}$

∴ Find the log of 3·682, multiply it by 2 and divide the result by 3 and find the antilog (i.e. find the log, multiply it by $\frac{2}{3}$ and then find the antilog).

This agrees with the rule we have already used, viz. to find r^n find the log of r and multiply by n, if n is a whole number, or a unit fraction; i.e. it now applies for $n =$ to any fraction. i.e. to find $(3·682)^{2/3}$, find the log 3·682, multiply it by $\frac{2}{3}$, and find the antilog.

6.51. Worked examples

1. $(3·682)^{2/3}$

No.	Log
3·682	0·5660 × 2
	1·1320 ÷ 3
2·384 ←	0·3773

$= 2·38$

2. $(0·0856)^{3/4}$

No.	Log	
0·0856	$\bar{2}·9325$ × 3	$-2 + 0·9325$ × 3
	$\bar{4}·7975$ ÷ 4	$-6 + 2·7975$
0·1582 ←	$\bar{1}·1994$	to 4 decimal places

$= 0·158$

6.52. Examples 30

1. $(4·982)^{3/2}$ 2. $(1·688)^{2/3}$ 3. $(0·0985)^{2/5}$

4. $(0·9643)^{3/4}$ 5. $(0·6871)^{5/2}$ 6. $\sqrt{(0·9971)^3}$

7. $\sqrt[3]{0·8641} + \sqrt[3]{0·9532}$ 8. $(0·00073)^{3/5}$ 9. $(0·86)^{1·25}$

10. $(0·773)^{0·2}$

6.6. Examples 31 (using well-known formulae)

(1) Simple pendulum. $T = 2\pi \sqrt{l/g}$.
    (a) Find T if $l = 3$ ft and $g = 32\cdot2$ ft/sec^2.
    (b) Find l if $T = 1$ sec and $g = 981$ cm/sec^2.

(2) Compound pendulum. $T = 2\pi \sqrt{(h^2 + k^2)/gh}$*
    Find T if $h = 32$ cm, $k = 41$ cm, and $g = 981$ cm/sec^2.

(3) Pendulum in magnetic field $T = 2\pi \sqrt{l/MH}$
    Find l if $T = 2\cdot6$, $M = 122\cdot8$, and $H = 0\cdot12$.

(4) Compound interest. $A = P\,(1 + R/100)^n$
    Find the final amount (A) and the interest when compound interest is paid on £850 for 4 years at $3\cdot5\%$ per annum.

(5) Cosine rule. $a^2 = b^2 + c^2 - 2bc \cos A$
    Find a if $b = 6\cdot78$, $c = 4\cdot83$ and $A = 48° 19'$
    Find A if $b = 7\cdot68$, $c = 5\cdot34$, and $a = 6\cdot66$.

(6) Volumes.   Volume of a sphere $= 4/3 . \pi r^3$ (take $\pi = 3\cdot142$)
    (a) Find the volume of a hemisphere of radius 3960 miles.
    (b) Find the radius (in inches) of a sphere of volume 1 cu. ft.

(7) Areas.   Area of a circle $= \pi r^2$. (take $\pi = 3\cdot142$)
    (a) Find the area of a circle whose circumference $= 68\cdot2$ cm.
    (b) Find the radius of a circle of area $2\cdot56$ sq. cm.

(8) Equations of motion. $v^2 = u^2 + 2fs$.
    Find v when $u = 56\cdot2$ ft/sec, $f = 4\cdot56$ ft/sec^2 and $s = 68$ ft.

(9) Electricity. $R = k \cdot l d^2$
    Find k, if $R = 0\cdot0028$, $l = 100$, and $d = 0\cdot75$.

(10) Moment of Inertia. $I = M\,(a^2 + b^2)/3$*
    Find I when $M = 125$, $a = 15$, and $b = 8\cdot6$.

* Note: In expressions of the type $a^2 + b^2$ the a^2 and b^2 terms can be found by logs but must be *added* together by 'ordinary' arithmetic.

Miscellaneous Examples

Take $\pi = 3{\cdot}142$

(1) $5{\cdot}2 \times 3{\cdot}16 \times 8{\cdot}64$

(2) $36{\cdot}82 \times 1{\cdot}965 \times 132{\cdot}18$

(3) $52{\cdot}2 \times 167{\cdot}3$

(4) $0{\cdot}48 \times 1{\cdot}963$

(5) $0{\cdot}0963 \times 0{\cdot}5822$

(6) $0{\cdot}0606 \times 0{\cdot}000384$

(7) $563{\cdot}7 \times 0{\cdot}0824$

(8) $0{\cdot}687 \times 1{\cdot}382$

(9) $6{\cdot}822 \div 19{\cdot}71$

(10) $483{\cdot}9 \div 77{\cdot}64$

(11) $\dfrac{3682000}{4748}$

(12) $1{\cdot}984 \div 0{\cdot}0828$

(13) $0{\cdot}943 \div 28{\cdot}6$

(14) $\dfrac{0{\cdot}0999}{8{\cdot}82}$

(15) $0{\cdot}686 \div 0{\cdot}00931$

(16) $\dfrac{0{\cdot}77}{0{\cdot}0452}$

(17) $\dfrac{36{\cdot}7 \times 0{\cdot}0886}{14{\cdot}9 \times 3{\cdot}142}$

(18) $\dfrac{553{\cdot}7}{16{\cdot}67 \times 0{\cdot}643}$

(19) $7{\cdot}078 \times 0{\cdot}0943 \div 0{\cdot}5656$

(20) $19{\cdot}43 \div (583{\cdot}7 \times 0{\cdot}9542)$

(21) $(1{\cdot}619)^5$

(22) $(0{\cdot}0535)^3$

(23) $\left(\dfrac{5{\cdot}64}{11{\cdot}16}\right)^2$

(24) $191{\cdot}2 \div (13{\cdot}98)^2$

(25) $\dfrac{(5{\cdot}62)^2}{(4{\cdot}93)^3}$

(26) $\dfrac{1}{\sqrt[3]{9{\cdot}834}}$

(27) $\sqrt[4]{0{\cdot}6543}$

(28) $\sqrt{\dfrac{3{\cdot}74}{9{\cdot}82}}$

(29) $\dfrac{4{\cdot}374 \times (0{\cdot}92)^2}{(11{\cdot}82)^3}$

(30) $\dfrac{14{\cdot}59}{\sqrt{0{\cdot}828}}$

(31) $\sqrt[4]{\dfrac{19{\cdot}18 \times 773}{4840}}$

(32) $(8{\cdot}688)^{1/3}$

(33) $\left[\dfrac{9\cdot42}{(11\cdot18)^3}\right]^{1/4}$ (34) $(97\cdot25)^{2/3}$

(35) $(5\cdot624)^4$

(36) Find the area of a circle of radius 9·84 in.

(37) Find the diameter of a circle of area 78·94 sq. in.

(38) The time of swing of a pendulum is given by $T = 2\pi\sqrt{l/g}$
      find (1) T when $l = 6\cdot5$ and $g = 32\cdot2$
             (2) T when $l = 384$ and $g = 981$

(39) Area of a triangle $= \sqrt{s(s-a)(s-b)(s-c)}$ where a, b, and c are lengths of sides and $s = \frac{1}{2}(a+b+c)$. Find the area when $a = 3\cdot18$, $b = 4\cdot26$, and $c = 5\cdot54$.

(40) Volume of a cylinder $= \pi r^2 h$, find r if $V = 983$ cc, and $h = 16\cdot16$ cm.

(41) Density $= \dfrac{\text{Mass}}{\text{Volume}}$
Find the density (1) if mass $= 562$ g and volume $= 13\cdot68$ cm^3
                     (2) if mass $= 3\cdot16$ lb and volume $= 5\cdot32$ cu.ft.

(42) Area of the surface of a sphere $= 4\pi r^2$. Find the area of surface of a spherical bubble of diameter 3·62 cm.

(43) If $pV^{5/4} = 500$, find p when $V = 103\cdot8$

(44) Angle in radians $= \dfrac{\text{angle in degrees} \times \pi}{180}$

     Express 44° 36′ in radians.

(45) In magnetism $F = \dfrac{2ml}{(d^2 + l^2)^{3/2}}$

     Find F when $m = 348$, $d = 11\cdot2$ and $l = 2\cdot95$

(46) Water flows through a circular pipe of 6 in. diameter at the rate of 27500 gallons per hour. Find the rate of flow in ft/sec, taking 1 cu. ft $= 6\cdot23$ gallons.

(47) Length of arc of a circle

$$= \frac{\text{angle subtended at centre}}{360} \times \text{circumference}$$

Find the length of arc subtending an angle of $121° \, 30'$ at the centre of a circle of radius 2·78 ft.

(48) The oil in a full rectangular tank 683 cm by 123 cm by 72 cm is used to fill cans of height 20 cm and radius 6 cm. Assuming 5% wastage of oil, how many cans would be filled?

(49) Using the formula $V = V_0 \gamma t$, find V if $V_0 = 5000$, $\gamma = 0·0000286$ and $t = 43$

(50) The radius of a circle of latitude is $R \cos \theta$ where

$$R = \text{radius of the earth}$$
$$\text{and } \theta = \text{latitude}$$

Find the circumference of the circle of latitude 55°N, taking $R = 3960$ miles.

Answers

Examples 1, page 5
1.	0·3010,	0·4624,	0·7634.
2.	0·4771,	0·2041,	0·6812.
3.	0·2304,	0·6021,	0·8325.
4.	0·0792,	0·3979,	0·4771.

Examples 2, page 6
1. 4·5
2. 4·8
3. 3·6
4. 5·4
5. 4·9

Examples 3, page 7
1. 3·8
2. 4·0
3. 3·5
4. 2·5
5. 2·0

Examples 4, page 11
1.	8·06		4.	7·50
2.	6·55		5.	1·25
3.	5·96			

Examples 5a and 5b, pages 13 and 15
1.	(a) 0·5593	(f) 5·994	
	(b) 0·6836	(g) 7·281 (2)	
	(c) 0·9375	(h) 1·294	
	(d) 0·8455	(i) 1·209	
	(e) 2·412	(j) 0·8010	

G

2. 0·6704   6. 6·62
3. 2·304   7. 9·62
4. 0·9718   8. 8·53
5. 1·206

Examples 6, page 17
1. (a) 7·134
    (b) 4·179
    (c) 3·405
    (d) 1·328
    (e) 1·918
2. 4·809
3. 1·209
4. (a) 0·4972
    (b) 0·8921
    (c) 0·4362
    (d) 6·054
    (e) 2·839
    (f) 1·666
5. 3·78
6. 3·39
7. 4·64
8. 3·93
9. 1·78
10. 2·07

Examples 7, page 20
1. (a) 0·8075
    (b) 0·5997
    (c) 3·616
    (d) 2·496
    (e) 0·0008
    (f) 0·3032
    (g) 1·830
    (h) 1·010

2. (a) 2·412
   (b) 6·753
   (c) 7·268
   (d) 1·029
   (e) 3·820
3. 4·80
4. 4·46
5. 6·18
6. 4·48
7. 3·00
8. 4·98
9. 3·13
10. 1·12
11. 1·66
12. 3·16
13. 2·37
14. 2·59
15. 1·28
16. 1·04
17. 1·68
18. 1·15
19. 1·47
20. 1·98
21. (a) 9·12
    (b) 6·55
22. 9·60
23. 1·69
24. 2·85
25. 7·75
26. $\log 1 = 0$, $\log 10 = 1{\cdot}0000$, $\log 4 = \log 2 + \log 2 = 0{\cdot}6020$,
    $\log 5 = \log 10 - \log 2 = 1{\cdot}0000 - 0{\cdot}3010 = 0{\cdot}6990$,
    $\log 6 = \log 2 + \log 3 = 0{\cdot}3010 + 0{\cdot}4771 = 0{\cdot}7781$
    $\log 8 = \log 2 + \log 4 = 0{\cdot}3010 + 0{\cdot}6020 = 0{\cdot}9030$
    $\log 9 = \log 3 + \log 3 = 0{\cdot}4771 + 0{\cdot}4771 = 0{\cdot}9542$

Examples 8, page 23

1. 8·29 inches
2. 2·62 inches; 1·31 inches
3. 9·73 sq. in.
4. 8·14, 1·59
5. 1·12 g/cm^3
6. 7·04 sq. cm.
7. 7·81 cm^3, 1·25 g/cm^3
8. 2·28 cm^3
9. 1·61 g
10. 1·40 g

Examples 9, page 30

1. (a) 1·58, $2^{1·58}$
    (c) 2·32, $2^{2·32}$
    (d) 3, 2^3
    (e) 16,   16
    (f) 9·19,   9·19
    (g) 128,   128
2. 1·86,   2·01
3. (a) 4·8   (d) 4·0   (g) 70·2
    (b) 36·0   (e) 1·97   (h) 15·5
    (c) 3·84   (f) 14·3   (i) 7·3
    (j) 8   (l) 1·4   (m) 2·2
    (k) 19·1   (n) 4·5

Examples 10, page 34

1. (b) 0·54, $10^{0·54}$
    (c) 0·96, $10^{0·96}$
    (d) 3·8, $3·8 = 10^{0·58}$
    (e) 4·2, $4·2 = 10^{0·62}$
    (f) 1·4, $1·4 = 10^{0·14}$
    (g) 1·05, $1·05 = 10^{0·02}$

2. (a) 0·66
    (b) 4·17
    (c) 0·62
    (d) 3·63
3. (a) 3·15 (d) 4·43 (g) 5·04
    (b) 3·36 (e) 1·50 (h) 3·54
    (c) 9·56 (f) 3·42 (i) 1·23
    (j) 2·28 (l) 2·01 (m) 5·00
    (k) 2·09   (n) 1·45

Examples 11, page 36

1. 4·5   4. 5·4   7. 4·0
2. 4·8   5. 4·9   8. 3·5
3. 3·6   6. 3·8   9. 2·5
                    10. 2·0

Examples 12, page 43

1. (a) 0·5000
    (b) 1·1747
    (c) 3·5879
    (d) 2·1753
    (e) 4·7226
    (f) 1473
    (g) 1·568
    (h) 21010000
    (i) 60·88
2. 36660
3. 2·5649
4. 4·9167
5. 1023

Examples 13, page 44

1. 202
2. 7320

3. 160000
4. 11300
5. 72900
6. 1·55
7. 26·6
8. 216
9. 3·58
10. 32500
11. 54·4
12. 6·43

Examples 14, page 45

1. 280 sq. in.
2. 227 cm³, 2·86 g/cm³
3. £175 10s. 0d.
4. 140 yds
5. 776 revs
6. 2070
7. 2·82
8. 3·24 : 1
9. 554 sq. cm.
10. 23·3 in.

Examples 15a and b, pages 52 and 53

1. (a) $\bar{2}$·9074
   (b) $\bar{1}$·7499
   (c) $\bar{3}$·6263
   (d) 0·000003848
   (e) 0·1878
   (f) 0·08999 or 0·09000
2. 0·4736
3. $\bar{2}$·9438
4. $\bar{1}$·9796
5. 0·4960

6. (a) $\bar{1}\cdot7523$
    (b) $0\cdot7584$
    (c) $\bar{3}\cdot9304$
    (d) $1\cdot2395$
    (e) $0\cdot00001676$
    (f) 6054
    (g) $0\cdot9084$
    (h) 470300
7. (a) $1\cdot9188$ (c) $\bar{2}\cdot9083$ (e) $0\cdot1937$
    (b) $\bar{1}\cdot9794$ (d) $\bar{1}\cdot9382$
8. (a) $0\cdot2216$
    (b) $0\cdot09080$
    (c) 800
    (d) $0\cdot0300$
    (e) $7\cdot705$
9. (a) $0\cdot03494$
    (b) $0\cdot7285$
    (c) $30\cdot47$
    (d) $156\cdot7$
    (e) $0\cdot1837$
10. (a) $1\cdot9361$
    (b) $\bar{1}\cdot5492$
    (c) $2\cdot9148$
    (d) $0\cdot2382$
    (e) $\bar{2}\cdot0000$

Examples 16, page 55

1. $4\cdot4363$
2. $1\cdot7050$
3. $4\cdot7949$
4. $\bar{3}\cdot8353$
5. $\bar{1}\cdot7585$
6. $1\cdot8363$
7. $2\cdot4179$ 9. $0\cdot5677$
8. $2\cdot9333$ 10. $\bar{3}\cdot9934$

11. $\bar{6}$·8413   21. 0·7561
12. $\bar{3}$·5495   22. $\bar{5}$·1585
13. 4·4443   23. $\bar{2}$·6059
14. 7·1204   24. $\bar{4}$·9432
15. 2·7420   25. 0·1262
16. 2·3364   26. $\bar{2}$·3455
17. 1·5209   27. 0·2973
18. 3·6012   28. 0·5965
19. 0·3934   29. $\bar{4}$·2646
20. $\bar{1}$·3456   30. 0·3236

Examples 17, page 56

1. 60·2
2. 0·950
3. 0·658
4. 0·00517
5. 3250
6. 0·641
7. 7·36
8. 0·000831
9. 45·5
10. 0·0946
11. 0·925
12. 2·51

Examples 18, page 58

1. 12·1 sq. cm
2. 3320 cm³
3. £4·265, or £4 5s. 4d. to the nearest penny.
4. 0·469 cm³
5. 0·243
6. 2·55
7. 3·21
8. 56·9
9. 2·99 cu. ft
10. 607·3

Examples 19, page 62

1.	1·2050	19.	1·6526
2.	1·1016	20.	0·7680
3.	1·1384	21.	3·8301
4.	$\bar{2}$·4738	22.	$\bar{3}$·9748
5.	$\bar{1}$·1371	23.	5·8701
6.	$\bar{1}$·2421	24.	$\bar{4}$·7996
7.	$\bar{4}$·6828	25.	$\bar{7}$·9202
8.	$\bar{2}$·1773	26.	$\bar{6}$·9084
9.	$\bar{7}$·5984	27.	$\bar{9}$·7552
10.	5·3915	28.	2·9226
11.	7·3131	29.	4·9574
12.	3·3703	30.	0·9127
13.	$\bar{2}$·5094	31.	2·3930
14.	$\bar{3}$·1341	32.	0·8272
15.	$\bar{1}$·4168	33.	2·8719
16.	2·5372	34.	$\bar{5}$·8030
17.	4·5704	35.	$\bar{2}$·4879
18.	2·0846	36.	$\bar{3}$·9433

Examples 20, page 63

1. $\bar{3}$·2889
2. 0·8754
3. 1·3639
4. $\bar{2}$·7487
5. 4·0000
6. $\bar{3}$·8853
7. $\bar{3}$·0991
8. 0·0882
9. 4·8146
10. 6·0956

Examples 21, page 64

1. 1·11
2. 297

3. 15·2
4. 0·0218
5. 1·25
6. 0·0603
7. 0·868
8. 0·127
9. 135
10. 0·0704
11. 21·2
12. 5·99

Examples 22, page 65

1. 0·804
2. ——
3. (a.) 0·0276
    (b.) 0·562 litres or 562 cm^3
4. 65·9 cm^3
5. 1·13 $\times$ 10^4

Examples 23, page 65

1. 2·53
2. 0·146
3. 3·64
4. 0·0309
5. 2530
6. 0·192
7. 0·0000778
8. 19·3
9. 0·00735
10. 42·0
11. 0·00456
12. 0·000202
13. 0·0909
14. 0·000650
15. 30·1

16. 0·0264
17. 0·0000238
18. 14·6
19. 1·50
20. 0·712

Examples 24, page 66

1. 11·6 cm
2. 0·00000180, 0·0631
3. 4·52
4. 0·812
5. 25·1 sq. cm, 1·99 cm
6. 50900 cm
7. (a) 4340 cm³
   (b) 4450 cm³
8. (a) 0·00578
   (b) 0·00555
9. 1·54 sq. in.
10. 0·271

Examples 25, page 70

1. 249000
2. 686000
3. 726
4. 59700
5. 875000

Examples 26, page 72

1. 0·144
2. 0·185
3. 0·0000850
4. 4·03
5. 0·0000000328
6. 0·551

7. 0·00130
8. 0·173
9. 13·9 (3)
10. 0·591

Examples 27, page 73

1. 2·99
2. 5·22
3. 4·44
4. 2·00
5. 2·85

Examples 28, page 75

1.	$\bar{2}$·3333	6.	$\bar{1}$·7824
2.	$\bar{1}$·6500	7.	$\bar{2}$·9648
3.	$\bar{1}$·3900	8.	$\bar{2}$·9017
4.	$\bar{1}$·6214	9.	$\bar{1}$·1249
5.	$\bar{2}$·7542	10.	$\bar{1}$·1859

Examples 29, page 76

1.	0·978	6.	0·315
2.	0·436	7.	0·220
3.	0·0988	8.	0·432
4.	0·954	9.	0·778
5.	0·237	10.	0·904

Examples 30, page 77

1. 11·1
2. 1·42
3. 0·396
4. 0·973
5. 0·392
6. 0·996
7. 1·937

8. 0·0131
9. 0·828
10. 0·950

Examples 31, page 78

1. (a) 1·92 sec
    (b) 24·8 cm
2. 1·85 sec
3. 2·52
4. £975, £125
5. 5·07, 58° 16′
6. (a) $1·30 \times 10^{11}$ cu. ml.
    (b) 7·44 in.
7. (a) 370 sq. cm
    (b) 0·903 cm
8. 61·5 ft/sec
9. 0·0000498
10. 12500

Miscellaneous examples

1.	142	15.	73·7
2.	9560	16.	17·0
3.	8730	17.	0·0695
4.	0·942	18.	51·7
5.	0·0561	19.	1·18
6.	0·0000233	20.	0·0349
7.	46·4	21.	11·1
8.	0·950	22.	0·000153
9.	0·346	23.	0·256
10.	6·23	24.	0·978
11.	775	25.	0·264
12.	24·0	26.	0·467
13.	0·0330	27.	0·900
14.	0·0113	28.	0·617

29. 0·00224
30. 16·0
31. 1·32
32. 2·06
33. 0·287
34. 21·1
35. 1000
36. 304 sq. in.
37. 10·0 in.
38. 2·82, 3·93
39. 6·75
40. 4·4 cm
41. 41·1 g/cm³, 0·594 lb/cu. ft
42. 41·2 sq.cm
43. 1·51
44. 0·778 radians
45. 1·32
46. 6·24 ft per sec
47. 5·89 ft

48. 2540
49. 6·15
50. 14,300 miles

Tables of Logarithms and Antilogarithms

	0	1	2	3	4	5	6	7	8	9	1	2	3	4	5	6	7	8	9
10	0000	0043	0086	0128	0170						4	9	13	17	22	26	30	34	38
						0212	0253	0294	0334	0374	4	8	12	16	20	24	28	32	36
11	0414	0453	0492	0531	0569						4	8	12	16	20	23	27	31	35
						0607	0645	0682	0719	0755	4	8	12	15	19	22	26	30	33
12	0792	0828	0864	0899	0934						3	7	11	14	18	21	25	28	32
						0969	1004	1038	1072	1106	3	7	10	14	17	21	24	27	31
13	1139	1173	1206	1239	1271						3	7	10	13	17	20	23	26	30
						1303	1335	1367	1399	1430	3	7	10	13	16	19	22	26	29
14	1461	1492	1523	1553	1584						3	6	9	13	16	19	22	25	28
						1614	1644	1673	1703	1732	3	6	9	12	15	18	21	24	26
15	1761	1790	1818	1847	1875						3	6	9	11	14	17	20	23	26
						1903	1931	1959	1987	2014	3	6	9	11	14	17	20	23	25
16	2041	2068	2095	2122	2148						3	6	8	11	14	16	19	22	25
						2175	2201	2227	2253	2279	3	5	8	10	13	16	18	21	24
17	2304	2330	2355	2380	2405						3	5	8	10	13	16	18	21	23
						2430	2455	2480	2504	2529	3	5	8	10	12	15	17	20	22
18	2553	2577	2601	2625	2648						2	5	7	10	12	14	17	19	21
						2672	2695	2718	2742	2765	2	4	7	9	11	14	16	18	21
19	2788	2810	2833	2856	2878						2	4	6	9	11	13	16	18	20
						2900	2923	2945	2967	2989	2	4	6	8	11	13	15	17	19
20	3010	3032	3054	3075	3096	3118	3139	3160	3181	3201	2	4	6	8	11	13	15	17	19
21	3222	3243	3263	3284	3304	3324	3345	3365	3385	3404	2	4	6	8	10	12	14	16	18
22	3424	3444	3464	3483	3502	3522	3541	3560	3579	3598	2	4	6	8	10	12	14	16	18
23	3617	3636	3655	3674	3692	3711	3729	3747	3766	3784	2	4	6	7	9	11	13	15	17
24	3802	3820	3838	3856	3874	3892	3909	3927	3945	3962	2	4	5	7	9	11	13	14	16
25	3979	3997	4014	4031	4048	4065	4082	4099	4116	4133	2	3	5	7	9	10	12	14	15
26	4150	4166	4183	4200	4216	4232	4249	4265	4281	4298	2	3	5	7	8	10	11	13	15
27	4314	4330	4346	4362	4378	4393	4409	4425	4440	4456	2	3	5	6	8	9	11	13	14
28	4472	4487	4502	4518	4533	4548	4564	4579	4594	4609	2	3	5	6	8	9	10	12	13
29	4624	4639	4654	4669	4683	4698	4713	4728	4742	4757	1	3	4	6	7	9	10	12	13
30	4771	4786	4800	4814	4829	4843	4857	4871	4886	4900	1	3	4	6	7	9	10	11	13
31	4914	4928	4942	4955	4969	4983	4997	5011	5024	5038	1	3	4	6	7	8	10	11	12
32	5051	5065	5079	5092	5105	5119	5132	5145	5159	5172	1	3	4	5	7	8	9	11	12
33	5185	5198	5211	5224	5237	5250	5263	5276	5289	5302	1	3	4	5	6	8	9	10	12
34	5315	5328	5340	5353	5366	5378	5391	5403	5416	5428	1	3	4	5	6	8	9	10	11
35	5441	5453	5465	5478	5490	5502	5514	5527	5539	5551	1	2	4	5	6	7	9	10	11
36	5563	5575	5587	5599	5611	5623	5635	5647	5658	5670	1	2	4	5	6	7	8	10	11
37	5682	5694	5705	5717	5729	5740	5752	5763	5775	5786	1	2	3	5	6	7	8	9	10
38	5798	5809	5821	5832	5843	5855	5866	5877	5888	5899	1	2	3	5	6	7	8	9	10
39	5911	5922	5933	5944	5955	5966	5977	5988	5999	6010	1	2	3	4	5	7	8	9	10
40	6021	6031	6042	6053	6064	6075	6085	6096	6107	6117	1	2	3	4	5	6	7	9	10
41	6128	6138	6149	6159	6170	6180	6191	6201	6212	6222	1	2	3	4	5	6	7	8	9
42	6232	6243	6253	6263	6274	6284	6294	6304	6314	6325	1	2	3	4	5	6	7	8	9
43	6335	6345	6355	6365	6375	6385	6395	6405	6415	6425	1	2	3	4	5	6	7	8	9
44	6435	6444	6454	6464	6474	6484	6493	6503	6513	6522	1	2	3	4	5	6	7	8	9
45	6532	6542	6551	6561	6571	6580	6590	6599	6609	6618	1	2	3	4	5	6	7	8	9
46	6628	6637	6646	6656	6665	6675	6684	6693	6702	6712	1	2	3	4	5	6	7	7	8
47	6721	6730	6739	6749	6758	6767	6776	6785	6794	6803	1	2	3	4	5	5	6	7	8
48	6812	6821	6830	6839	6848	6857	6866	6875	6884	6893	1	2	3	4	4	5	6	7	8
49	6902	6911	6920	6928	6937	6946	6955	6964	6972	6981	1	2	3	4	4	5	6	7	8
	0	1	2	3	4	5	6	7	8	9	1	2	3	4	5	6	7	8	9

Logarithms of Numbers

	0	1	2	3	4	5	6	7	8	9	1	2	3	4	5	6	7	8	9	
50	6990	6998	7007	7016	7024	7033	7042	7050	7059	7067	1	2	3	3	4	5	6	7	8	Logs
51	7076	7084	7093	7101	7110	7118	7126	7135	7143	7152	1	2	3	3	4	5	6	7	8	
52	7160	7168	7177	7185	7193	7202	7210	7218	7226	7235	1	2	2	3	4	5	6	7	7	
53	7243	7251	7259	7267	7275	7284	7292	7300	7308	7316	1	2	2	3	4	5	6	6	7	
54	7324	7332	7340	7348	7356	7364	7372	7380	7388	7396	1	2	2	3	4	5	6	6	7	
55	7404	7412	7419	7427	7435	7443	7451	7459	7466	7474	1	2	2	3	4	5	5	6	7	
56	7482	7490	7497	7505	7513	7520	7528	7536	7543	7551	1	2	2	3	4	5	5	6	7	
57	7559	7566	7574	7582	7589	7597	7604	7612	7619	7627	1	2	2	3	4	5	5	6	7	
58	7634	7642	7649	7657	7664	7672	7679	7686	7694	7701	1	1	2	3	4	4	5	6	7	
59	7709	7716	7723	7731	7738	7745	7752	7760	7767	7774	1	1	2	3	4	4	5	6	7	
60	7782	7789	7796	7803	7810	7818	7825	7832	7839	7846	1	1	2	3	4	4	5	6	6	
61	7853	7860	7868	7875	7882	7889	7896	7903	7910	7917	1	1	2	3	4	4	5	6	6	
62	7924	7931	7938	7945	7952	7959	7966	7973	7980	7987	1	1	2	3	3	4	5	6	6	
63	7993	8000	8007	8014	8021	8028	8035	8041	8048	8055	1	1	2	3	3	4	5	5	6	
64	8062	8069	8075	8082	8089	8096	8102	8109	8116	8122	1	1	2	3	3	4	5	5	6	
65	8129	8136	8142	8149	8156	8162	8169	8176	8182	8189	1	1	2	3	3	4	5	5	6	
66	8196	8202	8209	8215	8222	8228	8235	8241	8248	8254	1	1	2	3	3	4	5	5	6	
67	8261	8267	8274	8280	8287	8293	8299	8306	8312	8319	1	1	2	3	3	4	5	5	6	
68	8325	8331	8338	8344	8351	8357	8363	8370	8376	8382	1	1	2	3	3	4	4	5	6	
69	8388	8395	8401	8407	8414	8420	8426	8432	8439	8445	1	1	2	3	3	4	4	5	6	
70	8451	8457	8463	8470	8476	8482	8488	8494	8500	8506	1	1	2	2	3	4	4	5	6	
71	8513	8519	8525	8531	8537	8543	8549	8555	8561	8567	1	1	2	2	3	4	4	5	5	
72	8573	8579	8585	8591	8597	8603	8609	8615	8621	8627	1	1	2	2	3	4	4	5	5	
73	8633	8639	8645	8651	8657	8663	8669	8675	8681	8686	1	1	2	2	3	4	4	5	5	
74	8692	8698	8704	8710	8716	8722	8727	8733	8739	8745	1	1	2	2	3	4	4	5	5	
75	8751	8756	8762	8768	8774	8779	8785	8791	8797	8802	1	1	2	2	3	3	4	5	5	
76	8808	8814	8820	8825	8831	8837	8842	8848	8854	8859	1	1	2	2	3	3	4	5	5	
77	8865	8871	8876	8882	8887	8893	8899	8904	8910	8915	1	1	2	2	3	3	4	4	5	
78	8921	8927	8932	8938	8943	8949	8954	8960	8965	8971	1	1	2	2	3	3	4	4	5	
79	8976	8982	8987	8993	8998	9004	9009	9015	9020	9025	1	1	2	2	3	3	4	4	5	
80	9031	9036	9042	9047	9053	9058	9063	9069	9074	9079	1	1	2	2	3	3	4	4	5	
81	9085	9090	9096	9101	9106	9112	9117	9122	9128	9133	1	1	2	2	3	3	4	4	5	
82	9138	9143	9149	9154	9160	9165	9170	9175	9180	9186	1	1	2	2	3	3	4	4	5	
83	9191	9196	9201	9206	9212	9217	9222	9227	9232	9238	1	1	2	2	3	3	4	4	5	
84	9243	9248	9253	9258	9263	9269	9274	9279	9284	9289	1	1	2	2	3	3	4	4	5	
85	9294	9299	9304	9309	9315	9320	9325	9330	9335	9340	1	1	2	2	3	3	4	4	5	
86	9345	9350	9355	9360	9365	9370	9375	9380	9385	9390	1	1	2	2	3	3	4	4	5	
87	9395	9400	9405	9410	9415	9420	9425	9430	9435	9440	0	1	1	2	2	3	3	4	4	
88	9445	9450	9455	9460	9465	9469	9474	9479	9484	9489	0	1	1	2	2	3	3	4	4	
89	9494	9499	9504	9509	9513	9518	9523	9528	9533	9538	0	1	1	2	2	3	3	4	4	
90	9542	9547	9552	9557	9562	9566	9571	9576	9581	9586	0	1	1	2	2	3	3	4	4	
91	9590	9595	9600	9605	9609	9614	9619	9624	9628	9633	0	1	1	2	2	3	3	4	4	
92	9638	9643	9647	9652	9657	9661	9666	9671	9675	9680	0	1	1	2	2	3	3	4	4	
93	9685	9689	9694	9699	9703	9708	9713	9717	9722	9727	0	1	1	2	2	3	3	4	4	
94	9731	9736	9741	9745	9750	9754	9759	9763	9768	9773	0	1	1	2	2	3	3	4	4	
95	9777	9782	9786	9791	9795	9800	9805	9809	9814	9818	0	1	1	2	2	3	3	4	4	
96	9823	9827	9832	9836	9841	9845	9850	9854	9859	9863	0	1	1	2	2	3	3	4	4	
97	9868	9872	9877	9881	9886	9890	9894	9899	9903	9908	0	1	1	2	2	3	3	4	4	
98	9912	9917	9921	9926	9930	9934	9939	9943	9948	9952	0	1	1	2	2	3	3	4	4	
99	9956	9961	9965	9969	9974	9978	9983	9987	9991	9996	0	1	1	2	2	3	3	3	4	
	0	1	2	3	4	5	6	7	8	9	1	2	3	4	5	6	7	8	9	

	0	1	2	3	4	5	6	7	8	9	1	2	3	4	5	6	7	8	9
·00	1000	1002	1005	1007	1009	1012	1014	1016	1019	1021	0	0	1	1	1	1	2	2	2
·01	1023	1026	1028	1030	1033	1035	1038	1040	1042	1045	0	0	1	1	1	1	2	2	2
·02	1047	1050	1052	1054	1057	1059	1062	1064	1067	1069	0	0	1	1	1	1	2	2	2
·03	1072	1074	1076	1079	1081	1084	1086	1089	1091	1094	0	0	1	1	1	1	2	2	2
·04	1096	1099	1102	1104	1107	1109	1112	1114	1117	1119	0	1	1	1	1	2	2	2	2
·05	1122	1125	1127	1130	1132	1135	1138	1140	1143	1146	0	1	1	1	1	2	2	2	2
·06	1148	1151	1153	1156	1159	1161	1164	1167	1169	1172	0	1	1	1	1	2	2	2	2
·07	1175	1178	1180	1183	1186	1189	1191	1194	1197	1199	0	1	1	1	1	2	2	2	2
·08	1202	1205	1208	1211	1213	1216	1219	1222	1225	1227	0	1	1	1	1	2	2	2	3
·09	1230	1233	1236	1239	1242	1245	1247	1250	1253	1256	0	1	1	1	1	2	2	2	3
·10	1259	1262	1265	1268	1271	1274	1276	1279	1282	1285	0	1	1	1	1	2	2	2	3
·11	1288	1291	1294	1297	1300	1303	1306	1309	1312	1315	0	1	1	1	1	2	2	2	3
·12	1318	1321	1324	1327	1330	1334	1337	1340	1343	1346	0	1	1	1	2	2	2	2	3
·13	1349	1352	1355	1358	1361	1365	1368	1371	1374	1377	0	1	1	1	2	2	2	3	3
·14	1380	1384	1387	1390	1393	1396	1400	1403	1406	1409	0	1	1	1	2	2	2	3	3
·15	1413	1416	1419	1422	1426	1429	1432	1435	1439	1442	0	1	1	1	2	2	2	3	3
·16	1445	1449	1452	1455	1459	1462	1466	1469	1472	1476	0	1	1	1	2	2	2	3	3
·17	1479	1483	1486	1489	1493	1496	1500	1503	1507	1510	0	1	1	1	2	2	2	3	3
·18	1514	1517	1521	1524	1528	1531	1535	1538	1542	1545	0	1	1	1	2	2	2	3	3
·19	1549	1552	1556	1560	1563	1567	1570	1574	1578	1581	0	1	1	1	2	2	3	3	3
·20	1585	1589	1592	1596	1600	1603	1607	1611	1614	1618	0	1	1	1	2	2	3	3	3
·21	1622	1626	1629	1633	1637	1641	1644	1648	1652	1656	0	1	1	2	2	2	3	3	3
·22	1660	1663	1667	1671	1675	1679	1683	1687	1690	1694	0	1	1	2	2	2	3	3	3
·23	1698	1702	1706	1710	1714	1718	1722	1726	1730	1734	0	1	1	2	2	2	3	3	4
·24	1738	1742	1746	1750	1754	1758	1762	1766	1770	1774	0	1	1	2	2	2	3	3	4
·25	1778	1782	1786	1791	1795	1799	1803	1807	1811	1816	0	1	1	2	2	2	3	3	4
·26	1820	1824	1828	1832	1837	1841	1845	1849	1854	1858	0	1	1	2	2	3	3	3	4
·27	1862	1866	1871	1875	1879	1884	1888	1892	1897	1901	0	1	1	2	2	3	3	3	4
·28	1905	1910	1914	1919	1923	1928	1932	1936	1941	1945	0	1	1	2	2	3	3	4	4
·29	1950	1954	1959	1963	1968	1972	1977	1982	1986	1991	0	1	1	2	2	3	3	4	4
·30	1995	2000	2004	2009	2014	2018	2023	2028	2032	2037	0	1	1	2	2	3	3	4	4
·31	2042	2046	2051	2056	2061	2065	2070	2075	2080	2084	0	1	1	2	2	3	3	4	4
·32	2089	2094	2099	2104	2109	2113	2118	2123	2128	2133	0	1	1	2	2	3	3	4	4
·33	2138	2143	2148	2153	2158	2163	2168	2173	2178	2183	0	1	1	2	2	3	3	4	4
·34	2188	2193	2198	2203	2208	2213	2218	2223	2228	2234	1	1	2	2	3	3	4	4	5
·35	2239	2244	2249	2254	2259	2265	2270	2275	2280	2286	1	1	2	2	3	3	4	4	5
·36	2291	2296	2301	2307	2312	2317	2323	2328	2333	2339	1	1	2	2	3	3	4	4	5
·37	2344	2350	2355	2360	2366	2371	2377	2382	2388	2393	1	1	2	2	3	3	4	4	5
·38	2399	2404	2410	2415	2421	2427	2432	2438	2443	2449	1	1	2	2	3	3	4	4	5
·39	2455	2460	2466	2472	2477	2483	2489	2495	2500	2506	1	1	2	2	3	3	4	5	5
·40	2512	2518	2523	2529	2535	2541	2547	2553	2559	2564	1	1	2	2	3	3	4	5	5
·41	2570	2576	2582	2588	2594	2600	2606	2612	2618	2624	1	1	2	2	3	4	4	5	5
·42	2630	2636	2642	2648	2655	2661	2667	2673	2679	2685	1	1	2	2	3	4	4	5	6
·43	2692	2698	2704	2710	2716	2723	2729	2735	2742	2748	1	1	2	2	3	4	4	5	6
·44	2754	2761	2767	2773	2780	2786	2792	2799	2805	2812	1	1	2	3	3	4	4	5	6
·45	2818	2825	2831	2838	2844	2851	2858	2864	2871	2877	1	1	2	3	3	4	5	5	6
·46	2884	2891	2897	2904	2911	2917	2924	2931	2938	2944	1	1	2	3	3	4	5	5	6
·47	2951	2958	2965	2972	2979	2985	2992	2999	3006	3013	1	1	2	3	3	4	5	5	6
·48	3020	3027	3034	3041	3048	3055	3062	3069	3076	3083	1	1	2	3	3	4	5	6	6
·49	3090	3097	3105	3112	3119	3126	3133	3141	3148	3155	1	1	2	3	4	4	5	6	6
	0	1	2	3	4	5	6	7	8	9	1	2	3	4	5	6	7	8	9

Antilogarithms

	0	1	2	3	4	5	6	7	8	9	1	2	3	4	5	6	7	8	9
·50	3162	3170	3177	3184	3192	3199	3206	3214	3221	3228	1	1	2	3	4	4	5	6	7
·51	3236	3243	3251	3258	3266	3273	3281	3289	3296	3304	1	2	2	3	4	5	5	6	7
·52	3311	3319	3327	3334	3342	3350	3357	3365	3373	3381	1	2	2	3	4	5	5	6	7
·53	3388	3396	3404	3412	3420	3428	3436	3443	3451	3459	1	2	2	3	4	5	6	6	7
·54	3467	3475	3483	3491	3499	3508	3516	3524	3532	3540	1	2	2	3	4	5	6	6	7
·55	3548	3556	3565	3573	3581	3589	3597	3606	3614	3622	1	2	2	3	4	5	6	7	7
·56	3631	3639	3648	3656	3664	3673	3681	3690	3698	3707	1	2	3	3	4	5	6	7	8
·57	3715	3724	3733	3741	3750	3758	3767	3776	3784	3793	1	2	3	3	4	5	6	7	8
·58	3802	3811	3819	3828	3837	3846	3855	3864	3873	3881	1	2	3	4	4	5	6	7	8
·59	3890	3899	3908	3917	3926	3936	3945	3954	3963	3972	1	2	3	4	5	5	6	7	8
·60	3981	3990	3999	4009	4018	4027	4036	4046	4055	4064	1	2	3	4	5	6	6	7	8
·61	4074	4083	4093	4102	4111	4121	4130	4140	4150	4159	1	2	3	4	5	6	7	8	9
·62	4169	4178	4188	4198	4207	4217	4227	4236	4246	4256	1	2	3	4	5	6	7	8	9
·63	4266	4276	4285	4295	4305	4315	4325	4335	4345	4355	1	2	3	4	5	6	7	8	9
·64	4365	4375	4385	4395	4406	4416	4426	4436	4446	4457	1	2	3	4	5	6	7	8	9
·65	4467	4477	4487	4498	4508	4519	4529	4539	4550	4560	1	2	3	4	5	6	7	8	9
·66	4571	4581	4592	4603	4613	4624	4634	4645	4656	4667	1	2	3	4	5	6	7	9	10
·67	4677	4688	4699	4710	4721	4732	4742	4753	4764	4775	1	2	3	4	5	7	8	9	10
·68	4786	4797	4808	4819	4831	4842	4853	4864	4875	4887	1	2	3	4	6	7	8	9	10
·69	4898	4909	4920	4932	4943	4955	4966	4977	4989	5000	1	2	3	5	6	7	8	9	10
·70	5012	5023	5035	5047	5058	5070	5082	5093	5105	5117	1	2	3	5	6	7	8	9	10
·71	5129	5140	5152	5164	5176	5188	5200	5212	5224	5236	1	2	4	5	6	7	8	10	11
·72	5248	5260	5272	5284	5297	5309	5321	5333	5346	5358	1	2	4	5	6	7	9	10	11
·73	5370	5383	5395	5408	5420	5433	5445	5458	5470	5483	1	2	4	5	6	7	9	10	11
·74	5495	5508	5521	5534	5546	5559	5572	5585	5598	5610	1	3	4	5	6	8	9	10	12
·75	5623	5636	5649	5662	5675	5689	5702	5715	5728	5741	1	3	4	5	7	8	9	10	12
·76	5754	5768	5781	5794	5808	5821	5834	5848	5861	5875	1	3	4	5	7	8	9	11	12
·77	5888	5902	5916	5929	5943	5957	5970	5984	5998	6012	1	3	4	5	7	8	10	11	12
·78	6026	6039	6053	6067	6081	6095	6109	6123	6138	6152	1	3	4	6	7	8	10	11	13
·79	6166	6180	6194	6209	6223	6237	6252	6266	6281	6295	1	3	4	6	7	9	10	11	13
·80	6310	6324	6339	6353	6368	6383	6397	6412	6427	6442	1	3	4	6	7	9	10	12	13
·81	6457	6471	6486	6501	6516	6531	6546	6561	6577	6592	1	3	4	6	7	9	11	12	14
·82	6607	6622	6637	6653	6668	6683	6699	6714	6730	6745	2	3	5	6	8	9	11	12	14
·83	6761	6776	6792	6808	6823	6839	6855	6871	6887	6902	2	3	5	6	8	9	11	13	14
·84	6918	6934	6950	6966	6982	6998	7015	7031	7047	7063	2	3	5	6	8	10	11	13	15
·85	7079	7096	7112	7129	7145	7161	7178	7194	7211	7228	2	3	5	7	8	10	11	13	15
·86	7244	7261	7278	7295	7311	7328	7345	7362	7379	7396	2	3	5	7	8	10	12	13	15
·87	7413	7430	7447	7464	7482	7499	7516	7534	7551	7568	2	3	5	7	9	10	12	14	16
·88	7586	7603	7621	7638	7656	7674	7691	7709	7727	7745	2	4	5	7	9	11	12	14	16
·89	7762	7780	7798	7816	7834	7852	7870	7889	7907	7925	2	4	5	7	9	11	13	14	16
·90	7943	7962	7980	7998	8017	8035	8054	8072	8091	8110	2	4	6	7	9	11	13	15	17
·91	8128	8147	8166	8185	8204	8222	8241	8260	8279	8299	2	4	6	8	9	11	13	15	17
·92	8318	8337	8356	8375	8395	8414	8433	8453	8472	8492	2	4	6	8	10	12	13	15	17
·93	8511	8531	8551	8570	8590	8610	8630	8650	8670	8690	2	4	6	8	10	12	14	16	18
·94	8710	8730	8750	8770	8790	8810	8831	8851	8872	8892	2	4	6	8	10	12	14	16	18
·95	8913	8933	8954	8974	8995	9016	9036	9057	9078	9099	2	4	6	8	10	12	15	17	19
·96	9120	9141	9162	9183	9204	9226	9247	9268	9290	9311	2	4	6	8	11	13	15	17	19
·97	9333	9354	9376	9397	9419	9441	9462	9484	9506	9528	2	4	6	9	11	13	15	17	20
·98	9550	9572	9594	9616	9638	9661	9683	9705	9727	9750	2	4	7	9	11	13	15	18	20
·99	9772	9795	9817	9840	9863	9886	9908	9931	9954	9977	2	5	7	9	11	14	16	18	20
	0	1	2	3	4	5	6	7	8	9	1	2	3	4	5	6	7	8	9